MAR

GOLD RUSH

MARINE K: SBS

GOLD RUSH

Jay Garnet

First published in Great Britain 1997
22 Books, Invicta House, Sir Thomas Longley Road,
Rochester, Kent

Copyright © 1997 by 22 Books

The moral right of the author has been asserted

A CIP catalogue record for this book
is available from the British Library

ISBN 1 86238 010 4

10 9 8 7 6 5 4 3 2 1

Typeset by Hewer Text Composition Services, Edinburgh
Printed in Great Britain by
Clays Ltd, St Ives plc

1

Murmansk, Saturday 25 April 1942

It was two a.m. and bitterly cold. In the Arctic port of Murmansk that April morning there was no hint of spring or dawn. The sky was veiled by charcoal cloud. Flurries of snow swirled along the quay, whipped by an icy wind that bit at half a dozen Russian soldiers working in pairs at the dockside railhead.

Two lights, shaded by tubes of metal, cast swinging yellow circles on the snow-covered stone slabs and on the soldiers' rifles stacked tepee fashion beside a single railway wagon. The men, dressed in heavy gloves, fur hats and greatcoats down to their ankles, were unloading two-foot-long wooden boxes from the cavernous interior of the wagon, its door locked open. Two by two they carted the boxes twenty yards across to the edge of the quay, where they stacked them in lines. Despite the cold, the men were sweating, for the boxes were heavy: 120lb each.

Beside the quay in the dark waters lay a flat-bottomed barge and a sturdy tug. Away southwards, beyond the barge, loomed the shadows of cargo ships and cranes. Back from the railhead a line of warehouses ran off towards the town, which was bomb-shattered, blacked-out and dead. Even in daylight there was little to see or hear. Most of the wooden houses had been burnt. Skeletal brick chimneys marked their sites, like gravestones. A few concrete blocks stood with windows gaping and paint peeling.

To the west, the rumble of heavy guns and distant flashes beyond low, bleak hills were a constant reminder that the Germans were close, hammering at the Norwegian and Finnish borders a mere fifty miles away.

Two of the soldiers lifted the last crate from the wagon. Nearby, in the darkness, an officer stepped forward and shouted an order, his breath steaming briefly beneath the arc lights. Two other men slammed the heavy doors and walked across to join the others by the crates. There were ninety-three boxes in all, stacked along the harbour wall.

Another order. Four of the men jumped down off the quay on to the deck of the barge. The two remaining men began to pass the boxes down to them.

The officer, glancing towards the north-eastern sky, stamped in a useless ritual gesture to counteract the cold, slapped his gloves together and shrugged his collar higher. Pyotr Grigorenko was weary to the depth of his mind and body.

After eight days of travel, they all were. But they would endure, because they had no option, and because they knew their mission was almost over.

Only Grigorenko knew its purpose.

Hitler had occupied Norway in April 1940, extending German domination of the seas northwards to the Arctic, and then swept across western Europe. On 22 June 1941 he had invaded Russia. Within days all access to the West was barred, except for the sea route via Russia's remote Arctic ports of Archangel and Murmansk. One quick push eastwards by the Germans and their Finnish allies would have deprived Russia of even these two outlets. But in winter, across those hideous, snowy wastes of infinite woods and a thousand frozen lakes, there was no such thing as a quick push. The northern rail link from Moscow, though battered, remained intact.

At the time of the invasion of Russia, Britain had stood alone for six months. Everywhere on mainland western Europe Germany had triumphed. But Russia was not such an easy target. If she could endure, she could tie down Hitler's armies for months, years perhaps, and offer respite to beleaguered Britain. Churchill had therefore promised Stalin all the aid that could be spared. Supplies were to be sent in on convoys of ships ploughing northwards through gales and fog, edging between the Germans to the south and pack ice to the north, skirting the northern tip of Norway to Archangel and Murmansk.

Murmansk lay ten miles inland, in the Kola Inlet. For Russia, this estuary was of vital strategic importance. Despite its position north of the Arctic circle, it was ice-free all year round. The sea was kept fractionally above freezing point by the last dying touch of the Gulf Stream as it curled along Norway's northern coast, forcing back the pack ice that lay at most a hundred miles away. Only a few miles further east, the Gulf Stream gave up the last of its heat. Four hundred miles away in the White Sea, Archangel was blocked off by ice from December to June.

The first convoy had arrived in October 1941. By the end of the first year the convoys, sailing every two or three weeks, had delivered seven hundred and fifty tanks and fourteen hundred vehicles. Britain could spare little more. But in December America had entered the war. From then on, most material would be from America. Until June the following year all of it would go to ice-free Murmansk.

Stalin was an unwilling ally, united with Britain only by Hitler's assault, but he had at least agreed to pay for some of America's supplies. Grigorenko's task had been to accompany the first payment of five and a half tons of gold to Murmansk, and there to hand it to the British for delivery to America.

The journey from Moscow had been dismal. Once, there had been a line direct to Murmansk, but that was an age ago, when Hitler was still an ally. The route now lay six hundred miles north to Archangel and then on north-west another four hundred miles around the White Sea. Throughout the late summer German planes bombed the railway and Murmansk itself almost daily. Under cover of the long Arctic nights, convict labourers, emaciated bundles of rag, repaired the rails. They had not the strength to do it well. In Moscow, Grigorenko was told the journey would take two and a half days, but they had given him rations for five; and it had taken eight. The train had rolled at walking pace through the northern forests, past remote communities of wooden shacks – Belomorsk, Kem, Loukhi, Kandalaksha. The engine, its tenders stacked with three-foot fir logs, pulled just a single enclosed wagon. In one half lay the boxes; in the other half wooden benches lined the walls. Above them hung wooden bed pallets slung from chains. A wood-burning stove kept the men from freezing to death, but although it was red-hot for twenty-four hours a day, it never melted the ice on the inside of the truck. Grigorenko and his men had not undressed, nor even taken off their coats, for over a week.

Now, unshaven and stinking like goats, they had nearly completed their task. They finished stacking the crates on the stern of the barge, and Grigorenko looked up at the tug, a tough little workhorse with a tiny wheelhouse open at the stern. He shouted; in the cab a shadow moved and the ancient single-cylinder engine thumped into life. Grigorenko scrubbed the back of his glove along his stubbly chin, easing his frozen jaw, then shouted once more. The men clambered back on to the quay, walked over to their rifles, slung them over their shoulders and began to climb down again on to the barge. The last soldier cast off fore and aft, then jumped down to join his companions.

The tug's engine chugged out a more urgent rhythm. Leaving the gold riding high on the stern of the barge, the men gathered together in the well of the bows, seeking protection from the icy breeze. Tug and barge pulled away, leaving the dockside and its circles of yellow light, fading now as the grey dawn filtered through the scudding clouds.

On the nearest British cargo ship a muffled figure appeared on deck and waved. Grigorenko waved back. He was still waving slowly as the barge passed under the lee of a British cruiser, HMS *Trinidad*, moored off the dockside at a sickening seventeen-degree list, the result of a torpedo strike on an earlier convoy. She was awaiting repairs. No one was working on her yet. Grigorenko nodded to himself in satisfaction. He had carried out his orders: to be away early enough that morning to avoid attention.

Over the western hills, the guns were silent now.

He looked northwards, into the wind, across the flecked water. Ahead, seven miles up the inlet, hidden in the dusk and falling snow, lay his destination: HMS *Edinburgh*.

2

Aboard the *Edinburgh* no lights showed. She seemed asleep, a black hulk of turrets, guns and funnels. But directly beneath the bridge, in a large hall amidships, a dozen ratings stood talking quietly and sipping hot cocoa.

The hall was an aircraft hangar, one of two. When the *Edinburgh* was commissioned she was equipped with four Walrus amphibious planes that were used to spot enemy ships and also – if the opportunity arose – to bomb them. The Walruses were launched by catapult from the flight deck between the bridge and the forward funnel. After a mission each plane was lifted back on board by one of two fifty-five-foot cranes. The planes were then stored away, wings folded, in the hangars. But shortly before this convoy the Walruses had been withdrawn: their role was to be taken on by planes from aircraft carriers. The hangars had been converted to other uses: the starboard one was a storeroom, and the other, in which the ratings were now gathered, was a cinema, with chairs stacked round the bulkheads.

Among the ratings was a sixteen-year-old seaman, Mike Cox. About all one would have noticed of him, buried in his voluminous duffle-coat, was a pair of startling blue eyes and a frank, enquiring gaze, contrasting with the subdued expressions of his bleary-eyed mates. Like them, he clasped a mug of thick, unsweetened cocoa, part of a sailor's staple diet, as they all awaited further orders. They had been turned out half an hour earlier, four from each of the ship's three divisions – forecastle, top deck and quarterdeck. Despite the heat that spread through the deck from the galleys immediately below them, they were cold, and they wanted action.

'What we doin' up 'ere, then?' said Mike to one of the others, a lanky lad he had never seen before.

'What d'you think I am? A bleedin' prophet?' the lanky youth said, aggrieved, and took another sip of cocoa.

Mike shrugged and peered round the side of the hangar. He saw the chief bosun's mate, an imposing man of six foot four with a fearsome hook nose, looking over the rails and down the inlet. He admired the chief, Charlie George, a Yorkshireman, partly because he was a powerful figure who exuded strength and confidence. But it was also because he was one of the ship's four divers, and as such had a special aura that hinted at adventure, danger and mastery of an unknown and fearsome environment. The chief nodded and stared more intently. Clearly there would be work soon, probably unloading stores of some kind. But why at this hour? He withdrew again into the hangar and raised his mug of cocoa.

Mike Cox was from Poplar, the heart of London's docklands. His father, Harry, worked on the railway; his mother, Doris, kept a whelk stall. Mike had been born in 1926, a bad time to enter life in the East End; but he had been protected against the worst by luck and his parents' strength of character. All around him as a child there were families who had lost fathers and brothers in the Great War; but Mike's father, born with the century, fought at Ypres in 1918 and survived unscathed. All around in the 1930s there were men out of jobs; but Harry Cox kept his. Most families were large, whereas, whether by luck or choice, Harry and Doris had only two children, Martin and Mike.

His father had been the pillar of Mike's universe. Fortunately, Harry was a man of good sense. During the blackshirt business, when the East End was torn by riots between fascist and anti-fascist mobs, he had kept clear. 'Don't you listen to that Mosley feller,' he told ten-year-old Mike. 'It ain't the Yids and it ain't just the government what's responsible for this mess. It's that bleedin' 'Itler. If 'e starts something, you give 'im what for from me.'

Harry was also a man of some imagination. Often, when commenting on the harshness of life in Poplar, he would say to his sons: 'You two are lucky. You don't have to put up with what your mum and me did. Our life's 'ere. You can get out.'

Martin had done just that. He was three years older than Mike and joined the Navy in 1939. Twice he returned, self-confident and tanned, from tours in the Mediterranean. The sight of him was enough to convince Mike that he must follow in his brother's steps.

When war came, Mike was sent off with a gas mask and suitcase to a farm in Somerset, along with a trainload of other kids. He hadn't worried. Dad was immortal, and Mum had old Lil – Mrs Reynolds – and the rest of the street. But in December 1941 he'd had a letter from his mum: Dad had been killed at work by a bomb. Mike came back for the funeral. By then, America and Japan were at it as well. The whole sodding world was at it. His mother tried to bury her own and the world's tragedies in hospital work. Mike stifled his tears and said it was time to give the Jerries what for.

In February 1942, a week after his sixteenth birthday, he joined the Navy, which was glad to have him. He was five foot ten, broad-shouldered, with light-brown curls trimmed short above the ears, solid in both body and character.

Two weeks later he was aboard HMS *Ganges* at Ipswich for basic training in elementary seamanship. Mike was not a born leader, but he was tough and adaptable, with a self-possession and an easy charm that won him ready acceptance.

In the case of Derek Hoskins it won him a good deal more than that. Hoskins was a gangling, pimply seventeen-year-old, taller than Mike by a couple of inches, but no match for him in confidence or strength. He seemed to tire easily and was often depressed by the skivvying required of a young would-be seaman. With his ravaged skin, he was the natural butt of the raw comments slung back and forth by the other lads. Mike never joined in. On the contrary: he had seen enough bullying in the East End. It was an activity of which his father had sternly disapproved.

One day, when the boys were in their hammocks, after their tea, the talk turned to girls.

''Ere, 'Oskins,' came a voice from across the mess deck. 'You ever 'ad it, 'ave you?'

'Nar, course 'e ain't. All 'e's 'ad is the pox. Look at his mug.'

'Where'd ya get that, 'Oskins? Too many 'and-jobs?'

It was then that Mike stepped in.

'Leave off,' he said. 'Just leave 'im a-bloody-lone.' Then, in the silence left by his sharp words, he defused the tension with humour. 'Anyway, I dunno what you buggers are on about. 'Is complexion's like peaches and cream. And it ain't 'is face what the girls want, is it? I mean 'e's got a prick like a six-inch gun. Ain't that right, Peaches?'

It was a poor defence, but the first the unfortunate Hoskins had had. From then on Hoskins had become Peaches, and relied on Mike. The relationship worked for them both. Unkindness towards Peaches brought a swift and witty response from Mike. Peaches was still a cause for laughter, but it was no longer brutal, and he was grateful.

Before the war, the boy seamen would have gone on to Chatham for a further six weeks' training. But America's entry into the war had changed all that. Mike and a couple of dozen other under-trained youngsters, Peaches included, were needed on the Arctic convoys. They were given rail tickets and told to join the *Edinburgh* at Greenock at the mouth of the Clyde on 30 March.

The *Edinburgh* had been launched in March 1938, as a sister ship to HMS *Belfast*. When Mike joined her, she had already seen a good deal of convoy action, having been on runs to Malta, South Africa and Russia. She was a fine ship: six hundred and thirteen feet long, with four propellers. At full stretch her eight Admiralty boilers and her Parsons turbines could drive her along at a shuddering thirty-two knots. Her crew was over eight hundred strong. Her armaments consisted of twelve six-inch guns, and twelve four-inch guns, together with a scattering of Oerlikons, some torpedoes and a couple of eight-barrelled pom-poms. Some experts considered her under-gunned for her size. Fully laden, she displaced fourteen thousand seven hundred tons; Fiji-class cruisers had the same armament yet displaced only nine thousand eight hundred. As one of the more experienced galley staff told Mike soon after his arrival on board: 'She's a big ship, mate, but she ain't got much punch. But,' he added, prodding a finger in Mike's stomach, 'I wouldn't swap her. She's safer than some.' By this he meant she had more than her fair share of armour-plating, which was up to five inches thick along the most vital sections – boiler-room, engine-room and magazines.

It was something of a relief to Mike, therefore, to find that when in action he was to be assigned to the four-inch magazine, four decks down, where his task would be to heft shells on to the endless-chain hoists that lifted the ammunition up to the flight deck. There, conveyor belts carried the shells aft to the three sets of twin four-inch guns set at twelve-yard intervals down both sides of the ship. When he was on normal duty his time would be taken up cleaning the mess decks and performing the ancient ritual of 'holy-stoning' the quarterdeck – scrubbing on hands and knees with a large, square stone known as the 'Sailor's Bible'.

In the light of what happened later Mike would have been happy to holy-stone the quarterdeck for the whole war. But within a week the *Edinburgh* was on her way.

As the cruiser pulled clear of the Clyde, the crew had no idea which direction they were to go – south to the Mediterranean or north towards

Iceland and the Arctic? Only when she swung north was curiosity satisfied. On the mess decks, Mike overheard comments picturing for him the experiences he was in for.

The last convoy – what was it? PQ 13? The old *Trinidad*, she was torpedoed and only just made it into Kola . . .'

'Cold? Last time we went out we had to chip ice off the gun turrets. There was three inches of it all over from the sea spray.'

'Hammocks! What you want with hammocks, young Cox? You want to sleep near a hatch. Don't want to be caught too long below decks if we're hit!'

Then the captain's voice echoed over the intercom with the news that the *Edinburgh* was heading for Iceland, there to rendezvous with twenty-three other ships and head for Murmansk, forming convoy PQ 14. The *Edinburgh* herself was to be more than just a close-support vessel. She was carrying steel plating for the repair of the damaged *Trinidad*, material that the Russians were unable or unwilling to provide.

For Mike that convoy was a grim induction into the most awful of the Navy's wartime tasks. After the rendezvous in Iceland the route led north-east past two bare, rocky outposts, Jan Mayen and Bear Island, then on towards the pack ice. Mike felt the wind screaming off the polar ice sheets; saw mountainous seas smashing over the bows; and was sliced on the cheeks by spray that froze to splinters of ice in the air before it hit the deck. Now he understood why men sometimes refused to wear lifebelts – to be in those frozen wastes of water was to die of exposure in three minutes; better that death came swiftly.

On this occasion the ice was further south than usual. Sixteen of the merchant ships and two of the protecting minesweepers were so battered by it that they turned back. Four days later the eight remaining vessels were bombed by enemy aircraft, which veered off back towards Norway without scoring a hit. A U-boat torpedo blew up the commodore's ship, the *Empire Howard*. Finally, a gale struck.

Below decks the conditions outside created their own peculiar miseries. All portholes were closed and air vents pumped in hot air, but internal condensation produced a slow rain of drips from the overhead pipes and electrical cables, and the inside of the hull was covered with an inch of ice.

In addition it was never possible to get enough sleep. With no one wanting to sleep in hammocks, every mess deck was crammed with fully dressed sailors trying to find a space to lie down – on the deck, tables, chairs, tops of lockers. Only the fact that at any one time thirty per cent of the crew were on duty ensured that there was enough space for everyone to sleep. In these conditions the repeated calls to action were something of a relief to Mike. He had an unreasoning, youthful confidence that the weight of metal around him would protect him from catastrophe, and the activity deep in the bowels of the ship gave him a feeling of being part of a living entity.

This time she survived unscathed. The *Edinburgh*, shepherding the remnants of her convoy and preceded by the four British minesweepers permanently based in the Kola Inlet, had dropped anchor on 19 April, after eleven days at sea.

3

'Where's that electrician, then?' shouted Charlie George, the chief, suddenly pulling back from the railings. 'Electrician! Let's have you in position on that derrick!'

The chief looked out again down the inlet, then turned towards the huddle of boys and seamen in the hangar.

'All right! Out here! Stand by for barge coming alongside!'

Mike and the others stepped out into the chill wind. To either side of him, up and down the ship, snow flurries dusted the superstructure with white. On the warm deck below, however, it turned to slush almost immediately.

Now he could see what had caught the chief's attention. A launch – no, a tug – pulling a small barge. Even two hundred yards away he could make out Russian guards standing, their rifles slung over their shoulders. Behind them lines of wooden boxes. There was no well to speak of. The boxes needed no securing.

The tug pulled up beside an iron ladder that led up to the flight deck. The Russian officer came up first, unshaven and haggard. From a doorway between the two hangars stepped the senior executive officer and a communications officer who doubled as interpreter. Both men spoke briefly to the Russian officer. The exec nodded and went across to the chief.

'OK, Sparks,' said the chief. 'Get that derrick moving.'

The crane hiccuped sideways and its hook dropped to the deck by the top of the stairway.

'You!' said the chief, pointing at Mike. 'Yes, you! See that cargo net? Bring it here!

Mike went across to the side of the hangar and pulled out the wire-mesh 'spud net' and hauled it over to the chief.

'Finish the job, lad! Put it on the hook!'

Mike, fumbling in his gloves, did as he was told.

The net swung up and over the railings and down to the Russian soldiers waiting below near the lines of boxes.

'Right. All of you out here. When those crates come aboard I want them stacked over there.' The chief pointed to the corner of the hangar from which Mike and his group had just emerged.

Two minutes later the sling reappeared over the side, containing five of the boxes. Slowly they were lowered to the deck.

'OK, lads,' said the chief. 'Two per box. Go careful now.'

Mike and the lanky youth, whose name he discovered was Reg Warner, took the first. He noticed the rough wood, the metal bindings, the stencilling – 'CCCP', the Cyrillic equivalent of 'USSR' – and the rope handles at each end. The box was about two feet long, a foot wide and seven inches deep. If it's food, thought Mike, as he went to grab one of the rope handles, there ain't bleedin' much of it. And why two of us?

Then he found out. He and Reg, using one gloved hand each, failed to raise the box.

'Bloody 'ell!' said Mike. 'What's this lot, chief? Bleedin' lead?'

'Ask no questions, son. Just shift the box.'

Mike and Reg applied two hands, lifted and walked.

As they returned past the others hefting their loads across to the hangar, a thought struck Mike.

''Ere,' he said to Reg, 'they wouldn't want nothing with lead. Sure as buggery it ain't baked beans. You know what that is? That's gold!'

'Gold!' said Reg, 'What they want effin' gold for?'

'Don't be daft! We've been bringing the Russkies all the stuff to keep them going, ain't we? You think we're doing that for free? Nah! Course we ain't! Stalin, 'e's got to pay, ain't 'e? And no one wants 'is roubles, do they? Gold. Got to be.'

By the time the second sling load landed on the deck the whole work party knew of Mike's guess.

''Ere, chief,' Mike said to Charlie George, who was standing silently to one side now that the operation was going to his satisfaction. 'That lot's gold, ain't it? Old Joe's gold?'

'Ask no questions, son, and I'll tell you no lies.'

But as Mike walked away to rejoin Reg, he overheard the exec mutter to the chief: 'You making sure that stuff's coming up carefully, chief?' The exec gave a humourless laugh. 'If you drop any over the side, you know who'll have to get it.'

Mike cast a glance backwards and caught the chief's eye. No question about it: this cargo was valuable, all right.

Unloading the ninety-three boxes took an hour and a half. The work was hard, and talk died away. Only at the end, as the last batch of boxes was being cleared, did Mike overhear any further remarks. One of the cases was lying upside down on the damp deck. It had lain just long enough for its coating of frost to melt. As Mike and Reg pulled it the right way up, they saw that the large red CCCP lettering had begun to run. Drops of red fell on the deck.

The chief had been silent for some time now, but at this Mike heard him say with deliberate melodrama to the exec: 'Looks bad, sir. Russian gold dripping with blood.'

The exec gave him a look and raised his eyebrows.

'Bad omen, sir,' the chief explained.

The exec smiled wanly. 'Let's hope not, chief. Let's hope not.'

The chief's image was an unusually poetic one, and it stayed with Mike. He recalled the stories he had heard about the Russians. Bolshies. Revolution. Famine. Death camps. Secret police.

'Bleedin' gold!' he muttered.

'Eh?' said Reg.

'Bleedin' gold,' he repeated with a grin, realizing his own pun. 'Looks like blood on the top of the box. Didn't you hear what the chief said?'

They dumped the last box in line, completing a rough wall about two feet high and twenty feet long outside the hangar. As he turned, Mike saw the Russian officer holding out a piece of paper to the chief, who waved to call over the exec. A boy seaman was summoned and dispatched. Everyone waited. The exec made drinking motions with one arm. The Russian nodded and called down to his men, who came on board and crowded into the hangar. Cocoa arrived. One of the paymasters appeared, along with the interpreter. The paymaster looked at the paper still held by the Russian. He went across to the boxes, spent several minutes counting and recounting the boxes, then removed a glove, tucked it under an arm, signed the paper clumsily, resting it against his other hand, and handed it back. The

Russian gave a quick smile and spoke briefly to his men, who filed off down the ladder.

'*Dasvidanye*,' he said, and then in heavily acented English, 'Goodby-ee.'

He turned and, after giving a final wave, disappeared down to the barge. Mike heard the tug's engine start and, with a swirl of water from the propellers, the little work party headed back towards Murmansk.

'Well, it's ours now,' said the chief, as he walked across to the boys. 'But you lads haven't finished yet.' He looked at his watch. 'It's five-thirty now. Get below to your galleys, have some tea and sandwiches, and be back here in twenty minutes sharp.'

On their return the chief was standing by to welcome them.

'Right, you 'orrible lot. You on the end, let's have that bomb-room hatch opened.'

He indicated a hatch that stood between the two hangars in the centre of the flight deck. It was built originally to give direct access straight down through several decks to the four-inch magazine and the bomb-room, where the bombs formerly carried by the ship's planes were stored.

'What – we going to put that lot down there, chief?' said one of the lads.

'That's right. Good boy. And we're going to take it *very* carefully.'

The hatch lay open now, revealing a ladder that went down sixty steps to the depths below. Above the hatch was a small derrick with a pulley and a rope through it that lay coiled to one side.

'They want some help down there. Anyone here work in the four-inch magazine?'

Mike half raised his arm as if he was still in school.

'That's my action station, chief,' he said.

'Down you go, then. You know your way. You'll find the master-at-arms down there with a few other lads, and they want a little more help. No need to look at me like that, lad. I know you're not allowed in the bomb-room. But it's empty now. All you'll need is a pair of strong shoulders.'

Mike stepped over the lid of the hatch on to the stairs and climbed down past the Royal Marines' mess deck, past the four-inch magazine, past a tiny telegraph room and down into the bomb-room itself.

He reached the bottom and turned. There, waiting in silence along the bomb-room bulkheads, was Master-at-arms Perry and five other boy seamen. Among them was the drop-shouldered, acne-riddled Peaches, whose face lit up at the sight of Mike.

''Ello, Cocky!' he said. 'What you doing down 'ere?'

'Same as you, son,' the master-at-arms interjected. 'You'll see soon enough.' Then to Mike, 'They ready up there?'

'They nearly was, yes,' Mike replied.

Perry put his face around the door and yelled up the hatchway: 'OK, chief. Lower away when you're ready!'

'Mind your heads then!' came a shout from above. 'Here comes number one.' And within a few seconds, held in a double loop of rope, the first box appeared.

It was a slow business, unloading each box in the confined hatchway, but loading up above was even slower and, despite having to manoeuvre the boxes over a mass of pipes that ran across the bomb-room floor, the boys were having to wait between deliveries.

After twenty minutes the master-at-arms muttered: 'We're going to be here all bloody day.' Then he called up the hatchway: 'Hey, chief, can't you put two on at once? It's slow work down here!'

There was a shout of assent from above. The next load contained two boxes and the weight – nearly 250lb – took the crew up on the flight deck by surprise. Urgent shouts rang out from above, over the rattle of the pulley wheel.

Perry again stuck his head forward to look up the hatchway. He just had time to shout 'Christ!' and leap backwards, when a box crashed at his feet. He continued his retreat before an ankle-high cascade of splinters, leaving Mike the closest person to the point of impact.

The box smashed open and its contents spewed

across the deck. Out fell not only a slew of protective sawdust but also three bars of glorious, dark, lustrous gold.

Mike had never seen gold before. Unaware that the others were frozen in amazement, he bent down to pick up one of the bars. He could now see directly into the half-empty box. Inside were another two bars, making five altogether. Later, he was to work out how many bars there were in the whole consignment: four hundred and sixty-five.

At that moment, however, his attention was concentrated on just one. Like the others, it was rectangular, nine inches long and with bevelled edges, so that the top, a mere two and three-quarter inches across, was half an inch smaller than the bottom. The whole episode had for Mike a dream-like, slow-motion quality. The intensity of the experience seemed to give him all the time in the world, time enough even to get an impression of the markings on this particular bar: an oval crest of some kind containing Russian lettering and a hammer-and-sickle stamp; more Russian letters, followed by '9999'; a long number; and then a short number, that of the bar itself: KP 1926. He remembered that in particular, for it was the year of his birth.

The rest he would only understand years later – the Cyrillic letters for the USSR and NKTsM, standing for 'People's Commissariat for Non-Ferrous Metallurgy'; the '9999', which indicated a purity of one part in 10,000; the long number, which was the weight in grammes. The bar was what is known in the gold trade as a '400 ounce good delivery bar' – 25lb of gold worth some £3500 in 1942.

The most extraordinary thing of all was the bar's weight. More precisely, what staggered him was that the weight could be contained in such a small space. It looked and felt like a fortune.

The moment that to him seemed to have taken an eternity was over in a matter of seconds. Master-at-arms Perry recovered himself first. He had tripped back against a pipe, but not fallen, coming instead directly against a bulkhead.

He now took three strides forward over the pipes, reached over Mike, said, 'Oi! Hands off that, son!' and grabbed at it with one hand. He, too, was surprised by the weight, and had to lean on Mike's shoulder to stand up straight with it. Then he shouted up the hatch: 'Chief! You buggered one of the boxes! I'll have to order up a shipwright. Let's have that second one down – slowly!'

He turned his attention back to Mike. 'All right, son, get this lot to one side. Stand by, the rest of you, for the next box.'

As the box touched the deck he gave Mike a tap on the shoulder and told him to get a message to one of the ship's carpenters to make his way to the bomb-room.

The loading then went on as slowly as before. It took another two and a half hours to lower the rest of the boxes one by one and stack them round the bulkheads of the bomb-room. In the meantime a carpenter appeared, went away again, returned with some planking and mocked up a new end for the split box. While the last few boxes were set in position, he packed the bars back inside the broken one and put little metal brackets along the edges. It was not a great job, but adequate.

When all was finished it was mid-morning and time for a meal break. The master-at-arms slammed the bomb-room's six-foot iron door, pulled the half-dozen levers that made it watertight, locked the solid metal padlock and returned the key to the master key-ring, which was under the charge of a Royal Marine guard.

4

Later that day, down below in their mess decks, Mike and Peaches lay in neighbouring hammocks, a mere sixteen inches apart – the regulation distance defined by the pins in the bar to which the hammock ropes were tied. In one way the lull provided welcome relaxation. There would be no action stations unless there was a German bombing raid and of that there would be fair warning. It was worthwhile slinging the hammocks just to get some proper kip.

But in another way it was not so good. Imagination worked overtime.

'Cor,' Peaches said for the tenth time. 'Gold! You 'eld it, Cocky! What was it like?'

'I told you, Peaches.'

'Tell me again, Cocky. I like to 'ear it.'

Mike sighed. ''Eavy. Dull – not as glittery as gold should be. Know what I mean? Sort of soft.'

'Cor . . .'

It was a conversation that was beginning to try Mike's patience, but it had an endless fascination for most members of the mess deck.

A dour Scots stoker tried to put it into perspective. 'For Christ's sake!' he said. 'It's no more than it would cost to build a ship like this one!'

But it did no good. Everyone was fascinated by the gold. There was scarcely a man or boy who didn't come up with some insane suggestion of how His Majesty's Royal Navy could be relieved of just one of those bars.

'Of course, it's all accounted for. But what if we get hit? What chance of getting a bar out with us, or a box?'

'None at all, you daft bastard.'

'That door weighs a ton.'

'Hey, Cocky, what did it *feel* like? Heavy, eh . . . ?'

'Carry one of those, you'd sink as fast as the ship . . . Besides, how d'you get in the bomb-room? Bring the Royal Marine guard, the master-at-arms, the commissioned gunner in on it?'

'Nah – get a soap impression of the key, then sneak down when the dynamos are being turned over and the ship's all dark.'

Most of the talk was harmless fantasy, but beneath it ran a substratum of tension and unease.

The stoker himself put his finger on it.

'Gold, laddie! They say those boxes looked like they were bleeding. I dinna like it. Carrying gold – it's no what a fighting ship's for.'

'Get away, Jock, yer superstitious git. If you don't want your share, I'll 'elp you out.'

Mike took none of this seriously. But Peaches was different. He became both morbid and obsessive. When he talked, it was either about disaster or about the gold. Mike once caught his eye as he was fingering the identity disc round his neck. 'Know something, Cocky?' Peaches said. 'If we go down, this'll be like writing on my grave.'

Twice he slipped away to talk to a mate of his in the wireless cabinet near the bomb-room.

'I dunno why, Cocky,' he said when Mike asked him what he was up to. 'Just to be near it, I suppose.' Once he said, ''Ere, Cocky, you know one of them bars would pay my wages for an 'undred years?' And another time, 'You know the first thing I'd do with that bar of gold, Cocky? I'd buy myself a new face.'

Somehow, something insidious had entered this particular hidey-hole in the *Edinburgh*'s maze of rooms, cabins, offices, passages and companionways. From Mike's mess deck it spread. The gold cropped up in comments and conversation, like recurring symptoms of a disease. Nothing to put a finger on, but there was a new mood to the ship, a feeling of insecurity of which the gold became an unconscious symbol.

For instance, on the day before departure, Mike overheard a conversation between two of the galley staff serving at the other side of the aluminium counter with its countersunk food containers.

'A few more days now and we won't have no night at all.'

'Yeah. Then Jerry can have a clear run at us twenty-four hours a day.'

'He's sure to, ain't he, if he knows about this bleedin' gold . . .'

The *Edinburgh* left the Kola Inlet at the head of a thirteen-boat convoy, QP 11, on 28 April. Sailing with the *Edinburgh* were six destroyers, four corvettes, a trawler and, as temporary local escort, four British minesweepers, together with two Russian ones. On board the *Edinburgh* were Captain Hugh Faulkner and the convoy's commander, Admiral Bonham-Carter.

For two days the convoy made slow and uneventful progress. The only sign of the enemy was reconnaissance planes circling at a safe distance. The *Edinburgh*, the prime target in the empty convoy, forged ahead, zigzagging at about twenty knots. Her manoeuvres were designed to outfox any predatory German submarines, and to get her as rapidly as possible up near the pack ice, where U-boats found it difficult to operate. However, this sound reasoning was nullified by pure bad luck.

U-456 was waiting, under the command of Lieutenant Commander Max Teichert, who spotted the *Edinburgh* on the morning of Thursday 30 April. Unwittingly, the *Edinburgh* zigzagged towards him and, with a final turn, offered a perfect broadside target.

Just after four that afternoon, Teichert fired three torpedoes.

Aboard the *Edinburgh*, there was no warning at all.

On several of the mess decks hundreds of seamen, among them Mike, were having their tea. Peaches was nowhere to be seen. Mike, wondering if he had gone to the hospital for some reason – seasickness perhaps – had no sooner stretched out on top of some lockers, when one of the older sailors, a man known for his surliness, had claimed the billet as his own.

'That's my spot, Cocky. I'm off to get my tea, and when I come back I want you off of there. If you're not gone, there'll be trouble.'

Mike remained where he was. He didn't like to yield to pressure. For one, two minutes, he lay there, his eyes closed. He had no idea what action the sailor would take, if any, but experience with the man had led him to expect the worst.

He was not utterly taken by surprise, therefore, when the lockers beneath him heaved and his universe exploded. But it was only when he landed on the deck that he realized the reason. The whole ship boomed and shook from the explosion. The lights went out. At the same instant the mess doorway was lit by a lurid flash. The lockers from which he had just fallen shook and banged crazily; some flew open and spilled their contents. The deck tilted. When recalling his sensation later, Mike liked to say it was as if they were held in the hand of a giant, who tipped them slowly to port. All around, tables and chairs left their mountings. Men at their tea were thrown from their chairs on to the deck, against bulkheads, against tables and against one another.

Mike found himself under a table. It was dark. Everywhere there were shouts, curses and bangings. His right ear hurt where he had hit it against the table leg. He felt hot liquid on one hand and something sharp. Blood? No, tea and a broken cup. He was disoriented and shocked, but like most of the men, not badly hurt by the explosion.

It was this first explosion that did for the gold. The torpedo struck on the starboard side level with the foremast, just twenty feet from the bomb-room. It was a devastating blast which blew a thirty-five-foot hole through the armoured plating and through the tank of furnace fuel oil that lined the hull at that point, blowing the top off the tank. Inboard, a series of bulkheads and decks buckled outwards and upwards. The blast opened up the four-inch magazine in which Mike had so often worked, the bomb-room and the conning tower which contained the unit responsible for damage control. There, half a dozen men were on duty. Above, in the Royal Marines' mess, the deck opened wide under the force of the blast, lifting men into the air and spilling several of them down into the sludge beneath. Instantly, water flooded the magazine and bomb-room, forcing its way into the lower conning tower.

Within seconds the next torpedo struck – so soon after the first that few realized there had been two hits. It took off a section of the *Edinburgh*'s stern – fifty feet detached completely, rendering the two outer propellers useless and destroying the rudder. The quarterdeck peeled back like the top of a sardine tin, rolling right over 'Y' turret so that the six-inch gun slammed clear through the metal.

In the ratings' mess deck, forward of the first blast and above it, Mike wallowed on the floor, trying to regain his footing on the oil-covered lino. The emergency lighting flickered on, casting a dull glow over the scene, as fifty or so ratings slipped and struggled their way to the companion-way and the hatch above, while Mike looked around for Peaches. Where was the silly bastard? As communications messenger, he should be on his way to the bridge already. That was action stations for him, and he'd get a right bollocking if he didn't show up.

At the top of the companion-way, Charlie George appeared, checking on damage. As it turned out, close though they were to the point of impact, there wasn't much. The doors and hatches were closed, as they should have been, so the blast had been well contained.

'I'd better get down the four-inch magazine,' Mike said as the chief hauled him up.

'Forget it, lad,' came the reply. 'You won't get down there. I've just had a message from the bridge. Down the magazine, all round there, that's been hit. Closed off and flooded. Best thing you can do is stay here and start clearing up.'

Mike had a funny feeling about Peaches. Where had he been when the torpedo struck? He wasn't on duty. He should have been in the mess room.

What was the last thing he'd said? Something about the bloody gold again? He'd talked often enough about getting down there. It was as if he was drawn to the bomb-room. But surely he wouldn't have actually gone there? He might have gone through the Royal Marines' mess deck. But he would have had no reason . . . Wait a minute. There was a wireless cabinet down there. As communications messenger, he could have had a reason to get that far. Come to think of it, he had a mate who was a wireless rating, and he'd been down there before. Could be he'd sneaked down there again, off duty. Could be he was there now . . . but that was just above the four-inch magazine. And the chief had said the whole place was flooded, sealed off. Anyone in there would be a goner.

Not that there was anything to be done. The ship, if not stricken, was a shambles. She still had some life in her, but not much. All around there was confusion: the hiss of escaping steam, the distorted blare of loudspeakers, the shouted orders and the deck listing a few degrees to starboard with the weight of water that had flooded in. All Mike could do was help the others to set the tables and chairs upright again, and clean the food from the floor. Those able to go to their action stations had gone, leaving a dozen or so in the mess deck.

At that moment a petty officer poked his head around the door and said, 'You and you,' pointing at Mike and another of the ratings. 'Down to secondary damage control. Know where that is? Shipwrights', and double quick. You're messengers. They want information, fast. Move!'

Perhaps this was his chance to find out about Peaches. If there was any damage control there should be information available about casualties. He grabbed his duffle-coat and gloves from his locker in case he had to go up on deck, and ran down the companion-way and along passages still dimly lit by the emergency lighting.

He stuck his head round the door and said he'd been sent as messenger. There were two men sitting at an intercom; one was talking to the bridge. An officer arrived at the same time.

'What about Jim Goodall?' he asked, before Mike could say anything.

'You from the bridge? Didn't they tell you?' Jim Goodall was chief of damage control. Everyone knew him because, to set an example, he did everything by the book – always wore an anti-flash helmet and gloves, always had a lifebelt partially blown up, always carried a torch and knife at his belt. 'Jim was down in damage control in the lower conning tower. He just had time to say the bulkhead was blowing. Last thing he did was shout that the hatch was secure. They closed themselves in. They must have drowned within seconds.'

'I see,' said the officer, and then was silent.

'I think I got a mate down there,' Mike ventured.

'A mate, eh? In damage control?'

'No, I don't think so. What about the wireless cabinet?'

The two men looked at each other. One of them scratched his chin.

'Wireless cabinet? Yes, there are a couple of blokes in there. Sealed off. Watertight. All right so far.'

'Can they get out?'

Another exchange of looks.

'Not at present, old son. That wireless room's just next door to the four-inch magazine and the lower conning tower. And that's full of water.'

'Two blokes in there?'

'That's what the captain said. One will be the rating on duty. I don't know who the other one is.'

'I think I do, sir. Me mate, Derek 'Oskins. Can I talk to 'im?'

'Not yet, son. There's work to do. We want you to get aft. Find a party attacking a fire below "Y" turret.

No phones. See if they need any help and report to the bridge, communications officer. Anyway, you won't get through to your mate down here, but you might from the bridge.'

Mike, being from the top-deck division, had never been aft. He made his way up to the flight deck and then back past the derricks that had lifted the gold, past the three four-inch gun mountings and down to the quarterdeck, where he saw at first hand the extraordinary effects of the second torpedo.

He was blocked by a wall of metal bent like a wave rising twenty feet above him. Below him the remains of the quarterdeck hung over empty space. There was no fire that he could see, at least not here. He retreated, up the companion-way to cross the ship by the aft funnel, and snatched a chance to look about him.

The wind sliced at him, a Force Four north-easter. The *Edinburgh* was wallowing along at walking pace, listing at ten degrees. Despite the terrible damage to the stern, she was still under some power. There was no other vessel in sight, though the rest of the convoy couldn't be far away.

From the other side of the ship there came the sounds of hissing steam, roaring flames, men shouting, running. As he emerged from behind the control tower, he collided with an AB running towards the front of the ship. Behind, he saw a petty officer.

'Messenger from damage control,' he said. 'What about the fire?'

Behind the PO, down the port companion-way, smoke and steam billowed. The man's face was black and his gloves were singed.

'I was just on my way there. Tell them it's OK up here. It's the engineers who've got the real problems. A few casualties, no deaths – unless there was anyone in the admiral's or captain's quarters. Tell the bridge. I'll check the fire. My name's Davis.'

He turned and, grabbing the companion-way rails, vanished, his feet not touching the steps.

Mike ducked back along the deck and up to the bridge, to the communications office with its packs of radio and telephone equipment. Half a dozen men sat or stood before an incomprehensible confusion of speakers, dials and switches. There were two other messenger boys nearby.

'Report on quarterdeck fire . . .' he said to the first officer he saw.

Two officers, one sitting at an intercom, heard his report. Even before he had finished, the officer at the intercom was relaying his information to the bridge and to damage control. Mike overheard snatches of conversation. Priorities had emerged. Captain Faulkner was now in direct contact with secondary damage control. Situation in both strike areas stable. Some power. Rudder gone. A dozen dead. *Forester* and the Russian destroyers on their way. Any news of primary damage control? The four-inch magazine?

'I got a mate down there,' Mike put in.

'Oh, it's you, is it?' said the communications officer, looking up from his console. 'Secondary damage control said you might help out. Wireless cabinet, was it? There's something odd down there. Can't get any sense. Mate of yours, eh? We'll patch you through . . . Hello? Hello, wireless room? Can you hear me down there? Can you hear me?'

There was a long pause. Then a small, tired voice came through, distorted by the speaker.

'Yeah, I can 'ear. What's 'appening?'

'That you, Hoskins?'

'Yeah.'

'Tell us what happened, Hoskins.'

'Tired. Can't seem to . . .'

The officer covered the microphone with a hand and said: 'It was the same last time. He wouldn't say.' He removed his hand. 'Come on, Hoskins, lad. Do your best. Where's the wireless rating?'

'Still asleep, sir. Can't wake 'im up.' The voice faded and then came through strong: 'Water leaking through the door. Jammed. Can't shift any of the levers.'

'Don't try it, son. You got a few tons of water the other side of that door. You just stay as you are. We'll be down with you in no time.'

'That's all right, sir. I'm OK, but ever so sleepy.'

'Don't you bother, Hoskins. You go to sleep if you like. We'll be with you in no time.'

'Best thing for him,' said the other officer, leaning

over the console. 'Do you want to say anything, lad? We'd like to know what happened.'

Mike licked his lips. He leant forward. ''Ello, Peaches. Cocky 'ere. 'Ow yer doin', mate?'

'Cocky! What you doing up the bridge?'

'A bit of messenger service. What you doing down in that wireless room?'

'Well, it was . . .' There was a long pause. 'Gold, the gold.'

'I thought it was, you daft bastard. What did you think you were trying to do?'

'I don't know. Just 'ad this mate on wireless. Thought I could chat 'im up and work out the door. I dunno why. You know. Like we was talking about. I thought if someone 'ad left it open. I thought . . .'

'You daft bastard! I told you you'd never . . .'

'No. I wasn't going to *nick* it, Cocky. I just wanted to look at it again. I started to chat up old Sparks here . . . I think I'm going to 'ave to go to sleep, Cocky . . . and then there was a bang and everything was all over the place and we was in the dark for a bit and then the lights came on. We thought we was all right. Then we 'eard the noises from next door and then we didn't 'ear no more after that.'

The room seemed to have gone very quiet. Mike glanced at the officer standing by his side. He couldn't have been more than twenty-six. The man at the console said, 'OK, Hoskins. There's nothing more you can do. If you want to sleep, sleep now. We'll have you out of there in no time.'

He threw the switch up. Mike was puzzled: 'What's up? Why is 'e so tired?'

'Not sure. First time he said that, we reported it. We reckon it's carbon monoxide leaking through from a freeze-box next door. That would knock him out after a bit.'

''Ow long will it take to get 'im out?'

The man standing up turned away. The officer at the console looked at Mike. 'He should have air enough for three or four hours.'

'But 'ow long . . . ?'

'Listen. That wireless cabinet gives on to damage control. Damage control is flooded and there were six men in there. The whole area is open to the sea. There's a hole the size of a bus in the ship's side. Out there, there's a U-boat waiting to finish us off. You want me to tell you the truth, lad? Or would you like to live with a lie for a while?'

Suddenly Mike understood.

He reached forward and flicked the switch down. 'Peaches!' he shouted. There was no sound but the hiss of the speaker.

'Leave it,' said the officer behind him. 'He's asleep. It's best that way.'

By the time Mike was back on his mess deck, four destroyers – two British, the *Foresight* and the *Forester*, and two Russian – had peeled away from the main convoy to provide the *Edinburgh* with cover. An attempt to tow her failed when the line broke, and in any case the destroyers needed to range free to provide protection.

The *Edinburgh* could make straight-line progress of a sort only by driving forward on both remaining screws and then reversing her starboard propeller to correct her course. For the next twenty-three hours her pace was pathetically slow: two knots. But at least she was not a sitting duck, and in addition Faulkner managed to correct her list by ordering the flooding of several compartments on the port side, thus balancing the weight of water in the damaged section on the starboard side. At the same time, however, this put the ship seven feet lower in the water.

Meanwhile the rest of the convoy had been under attack by German torpedo-carrying planes, at least four submarines and three destroyers, the *Hermann Schoemann*, *Z24* and *Z25*. The destroyers sank the Russian trawler and were then ordered to finish off the crippled *Edinburgh*.

By then the two Russian destroyers had left for the Kola Inlet. They said they were running out of fuel, which was no doubt true; but they also pointed out that 1 May was an official holiday in Russia and that they would be unable to make an immediate return.

There were compensations. A Russian tug, the *Rubin*, appeared, along with four British minesweepers from the main convoy. With the minesweepers circling her protectively, the *Rubin* steadied the *Edinburgh*'s course by pulling to starboard and a minesweeper threw a line to her stern to act as a drogue. With this assistance the *Edinburgh* limped back towards the Kola Inlet at a steady three knots.

Early on 2 May the three German destroyers emerged from scudding snow showers to finish off the *Edinburgh*. Faulkner at once released the tow-ships and ordered full steam ahead – eight knots – driving round in a fixed circle to port, but still able to fight. Indeed, with her second salvo from her remaining six-inch guns, she struck the *Hermann Schoemann*, bringing her to a standstill.

Meanwhile the *Forester* had been hit by *Z24*, and brought to a temporary halt, her boiler room and bridge shattered. *Z25* attempted to finish her off with a fan of torpedoes. Fortunately, they ran too deep and passed clear underneath her. Slowly, shielded by smoke from the *Foresight*, the *Forester* got underway again.

But the torpedoes were still running clear. Beyond the *Forester*, they surfaced. Way ahead, the *Edinburgh* pursued her eight-knot fixed circle.

Mike was up in the flight deck, watching the action, when he saw the torpedoes, four of them, bouncing along on the surface like dolphins, their wakes streaming out behind them. He and the other lads with him yelled and pointed.

By then the torpedo tracks had been spotted from the bridge. Faulkner ordered full steam ahead on the one propeller and astern on the other, to turn the *Edinburgh*, and then ordered the engine-room to be abandoned.

As the wakes of the torpedoes approached, the *Edinburgh*'s bows slowly swung away from them, presenting a narrower and narrower target. By the time the torpedoes reached her, she had reduced her effective width by two-thirds, and three of the torpedoes passed her harmlessly.

The fourth did not. It hit the port side, almost exactly opposite the spot at which the first torpedo had struck. A cascade of water shot up over the side of the vessel. Mike and the rest of the men on deck were nearly deafened by the blast, but had tight hold of railings and companion-ways, which prevented them from falling as the stricken ship reared.

The torpedo almost cut her in two. Because she was seven feet lower in the water, the torpedo entered above her armour plating and exploded in her abandoned engine-room.

As she began to list to port, Mike shouted, 'That's it! We're going!' Across his mind there raced suddenly the stories of what happened to you in the Arctic waters – frostbite in two minutes, death in three. He refused to contemplate the idea that he would die, but didn't fancy risking frostbite. Immediately across from him was the starboard hangar, the one being used as a store. Inside, he knew, were some tins of engine grease, and with a shout of 'Come on, lads!' to his shipmates, he dashed across to the tins, grabbed one, forced off a lid and began to daub it on his hands and face. The other four watched him in amazement, but refused to follow suit.

At that moment Charlie George ran past and, spotting them, turned and shouted, 'Come on, you lads! Get down to your mess decks! Get your gear together!'

But they didn't go below. They all had lifebelts on, and didn't want to risk being trapped.

It was clear that the *Edinburgh* was doomed. The six-inch guns were still firing, but she was listing more and more heavily to port. Further down the flight deck, Mike saw a score of sailors trying to put out a thirty-two-foot cutter. Others had begun to unship the four starboard Carley floats. Someone shouted, 'One, two, six!' and one of the floats sailed over the side. No one had secured it, and it hit the water with a splash and vanished slowly astern.

Suddenly there was the chief again at his duty station on the flight deck, shouting down the starboard side to the men struggling with the cutter and beyond them to the others with the Carley floats. 'Get those inboard! Minesweepers coming alongside! Prepare to abandon ship!'

The word had already been passed below decks. Men streamed from every doorway, crossing on to the flight deck, on to the starboard side in an automatic attempt to counteract the port list, now so severe that the six-inch guns could not be brought to bear and had fallen silent. Even the weight of eight hundred men could not do much to rectify a list in ten thousand tons of metal, but as they crowded up against the railings, one diminutive sailor who went across the sloping deck to view the battle from the other side drew shouts from a score of his mate. 'Come over 'ere, you daft bastard, you'll tip us over.'

By now the German destroyers were less interested in the *Edinburgh* than in rescuing their own country-men from the crippled *Hermann Schoemann*. A British minesweeper, the *Hussar*, laid a smokescreen between the British and the German forces, and two other minesweepers drew up alongside the *Edinburgh*. First to arrive, on the starboard side, was the *Gossamer*, which took aboard four hundred and forty officers and men. Another three hundred and fifty left by the port side on to the *Harrier*.

In the circumstances, the evacuation was surpris-ingly orderly. Mike helped to carry the twenty-three wounded from below decks, across to the *Harrier*, on to which he also stepped. The weather was kind: the ships moved only a little in the swell, and the stretchers of the wounded were easily handed from one to the other.

The *Harrier* then stood off and was given the task of scuttling the *Edinburgh*, to prevent the ship and its gold cargo falling into enemy hands.

Still protected by the *Forester*, the *Foresight* and the *Hussar*'s smokescreen, she lobbed depth-charges up against the *Edinburgh* amidships in an attempt to break her back. The explosions had no effect other than to drench the *Edinburgh*'s decks with water. *Harrier*'s gunners then put some four-inch shells into her point-blank, succeeding only in blowing up one of the pom-poms.

Mike was watching from the *Harrier*'s deck.

'Ere,' he said. 'She ain't goin' to go, after all. The Jerries are buggering off. What say we get back on and save her?' It was only a joke, but as he said it, it crossed his mind that somewhere entombed in the *Edinburgh* was poor old Peaches. Perhaps he'd had enough air to survive. Perhaps the wireless cabinet was still not flooded.

'No, mate. You can see she won't last. But we've got to do for her quick as possible, or the Jerries'll come back for her.'

Finally, while the *Gossamer* made for Murmansk, the *Harrier* laid off to supervise the *Edinburgh*'s final dispatch.

It was done with a torpedo from the *Foresight*. The smoke had cleared. There was no sign of any German vessel. The *Hermann Schoemann*'s crew had been saved, and she herself scuttled, for the same reason as the *Edinburgh*.

The *Foresight*'s torpedo struck the listing *Edinburgh* in the forward boiler-room. This time the explosion was lethal, for a boiler-room cannot be divided off by bulkheads and decks, and the huge hall, stuffed with a maze of boilers and pipes, tubes, wires and dials would accommodate so much water that there could be no hope of saving her.

Mike, emotionally stricken but otherwise unharmed, watched the death of the *Edinburgh* from the *Harrier*'s quarterdeck. It happened extraordinarily quickly. In less than a minute the great boiler-room filled sufficiently to roll the Edinburgh slowly over on to her port side.

Then, without any further explosions and with a steady dignity, her battered stern sank. Her forward section, well sealed against the effects of any of the three torpedoes, was as buoyant as ever. As the stern went down she tilted to a seemingly impossible angle, until sixty feet of her bows were pointing straight up in the air.

Then she began her descent, slipping steadily beneath the waves. But before her final departure, something strange occurred. Held up briefly by the air pocket in her bows, she paused with her 'A' turret of three six-inch guns pointing skywards like fingers reaching for help. In later life Mike came to call this her 'curtsey', a brief, formal farewell before she resumed her descent and the waves closed gently over her.

In the light of later events her strangely placid burial was extremely fortunate. The Barents Sea at this position is eight hundred feet deep. A ship of some ten thousand tons, descending at a shallow angle in that depth of water, would normally have picked up a considerable speed. When she hit the bottom, she would have buckled. Bulkheads would have collapsed, decks bent and any remaining cargo been shaken and crushed beneath the weight of metal. But with the *Edinburgh* this did not happen. She was herself over six hundred feet long. When she finally sank beneath the waves she was vertical and her stern was only two hundred feet from the seabed. By the time she had begun to pick up any speed, the buckled stern was touching the bottom. The rest of her, still borne up by the tremendous pressure of water trapped in her bows, pivoted lazily downwards, depositing her on her port side on the ocean floor.

Her sinking caused almost no further damage. The inner bulkheads of the bomb-room remained intact. The gold boxes tumbled over each other as the bomb-room floor became its new wall. Two or three bodies from the lower conning tower drifted down through the hole blasted by the first torpedo, and on into the bomb-room. They were joined by shells from the four-inch magazine. But except for the torpedo damage, she remained to all intents and purposes in perfect condition. Even the wooden thirty-two-foot cutter that had proved so obdurate, remained intact. It was as if the *Edinburgh*, in a final gesture to her country, had arranged to die in the most convenient possible position for future salvors.

Though no one knew it at the time, all that had

to be done to reach the gold was make a long arm from the surface.

It was to take nearly forty years before anyone knew how to make an arm long enough.

5

Like many of the older men around him, Mike wept at the loss of the *Edinburgh*. If he had been asked why, he would probably have denied the tears. If pressed, he might have said they were for Peaches, the poor daft bastard. But, of course, it was much more than that. For the past few weeks the *Edinburgh* had been his whole world. For every seaman a ship becomes a living thing. The complexity of her, the fact that for ninety-nine per cent of the time she works with her subsidiary elements – junior officers, cooks, engineers, communications staff, gunner personnel, all the separate divisions and watches – knowing nothing at all about what the others are doing, makes her at once like both a human body and a city. The information that flows through the ship and the services that make her function seem to operate automatically, suggesting the notion that she is alive and in control of her own destiny. Which was why, as well as mourning Peaches and the loss of other lives, Mike also mourned the *Edinburgh* herself.

That stage did not last long. He was young, resilient and, above all, safe. He was also cold, tired – he had not slept more than a few hours in four days – and very hungry. Physical need superseded emotional distress.

Though three hundred and fifty mouths were a lot extra to accommodate aboard a minesweeper, it was not far to the Kola Inlet – twelve hours – and the galley staff set about making food and cocoa for the new arrivals.

Below decks, warm again, Mike crowded into a mess room with scores of others, all as bemused as himself. He began to pick out other boy seamen from his own mess deck on the *Edinburgh* and joined them. They talked about what they had experienced over the past three days. They had all aged. They had faced the possibility of death for the first time, and had survived, acquiring a certain stature as a result.

This was dramatized by one little incident. One of the minesweeper's ABs came in to dispense tots of rum. Mike was not used to spirits. He had tried the odd sipper and gulper – the two quantities of rum that formed a sort of alcoholic currency aboard – but had been more put off by the pain of the rough liquid coursing down his throat than attracted by the heady after-effects. This time, however, he had little choice. He was on the point of refusing his tot when an officious mess lieutenant glanced over the heads of the survivors and said to the

AB, 'You can't give any to those lads! They're under age!'

At this moment Mike saw Charlie George for the first time. The chief overheard the comment and his response was instantaneous. 'Forget the bloody regulations! These lads have just come off a sinking ship. They deserve their tot, same as the rest of us!'

There weren't enough tin mugs to go round and Mike had to swig the rum in one gulp. To someone unused to alcohol, and with an empty stomach, the effects were rapid. He downed his cocoa, lay down on the deck by a locker, pulled the hood of his duffle-coat up to soften the metal beneath his head, and fell asleep.

The run back to the Kola Inlet was uneventful. He slept for eight solid hours, awoke only to relieve himself, picking his way back to his billet over the exhausted, silent bodies of his shipmates, and slept again. By the time he had collected some soup and bread for breakfast on the morning of 3 May, the *Harrier* was approaching the inlet that he had left in the *Edinburgh* just five days before.

The two minesweepers moored just inside the mouth of the inlet, alongside the dock at the Polyarnyo naval base. That first stop on Russian soil was a brief one. The survivors assembled ashore. Faulkner called the roll on the dockside, establishing that seven hundred and ninety of the *Edinburgh*'s eight hundred and fifty crew had been successfully evacuated.

At Polyarnyo the senior officers were billeted until they could be found flights home on the British bombers that landed in Norway for refuelling after raiding the German airfields. The ratings remained only long enough to draw replacement hats, coats, boots and gloves from the British stores there. Then they were re-embarked – there was no room to billet them ashore – and the following day were taken five miles further down the inlet to the Russian camp at Vaenga.

Here, the seven hundred and fifty crew were housed in conditions so primitive that Mike could only think fondly of East End slums and the hugger-mugger friendliness of the *Edinburgh*'s mess deck. On arrival he was ordered into a gang of a hundred by a sturdy Russian officer, who was, he realized after several minutes, a woman. Speaking in abrupt and distorted English, she lined them up on the dockside, then marched them up through lines of wooden houses to a large hall set on the snowy hillside. Inside, the hall was empty save for a single stove. At the far end was what had once been a stage. Six feet above it, over the same area, was a second floor. In the corner of the hall was a pile of sacks. 'Take bags!' the woman shouted. 'Go outside! You see spades, sawdust! You fill bags with sawdust! This is mattress!'

'Sawdust' turned out to be something of a

euphemism. The pile of dust and chippings outside contained blocks of wood up to two inches square, some of them with nails in. But it was all there was. Within an hour Mike and his companions had made their crude mattresses. As they filed back inside the hall the woman was pointing to the stage and the floor above it. 'Fifty men down here! Fifty men up here! You sleep!'

The hall was one focal point of their lives for the next few weeks. The other was the mess-house down the hillside. The food was revolting – greasy tea and bread so stodgy that, as several survivors proved to their satisfaction, it stuck when thrown at the walls.

But the Russians had nothing else to offer, and were keen to save on even this appalling fare. On the first day some of the men found themselves physically unable to consume all of their portion. The next day the amount of food delivered to their table was cut by precisely the amount that had been left the previous day. After a week of this the rations of some tables had been cut by about twenty per cent. By then the men were so hungry that they would have eaten anything. They protested. Through interpreters the Russian officers claimed it was too late – the men had themselves decided how much they wished to eat and could not change their minds now. Only when it became clear that the British still had the strength to riot, and would do so, did the Russians capitulate and reinstitute the original amount of their stomach-turning rations.

There were no toilets. At first this didn't seem so bad, because urine and faeces simply melted holes in the snow, vanished and froze solid. But spring was coming. Within two weeks, by the middle of May, the snow was mostly gone. During the day the top soil began to thaw. The stench that then arose around the camp was appalling. It was also a health hazard. The master-at-arms, acting as spokesman for all the men, persuaded the camp commandant to provide a few dozen shovels. As spring turned into summer, work parties dug out a twelve-foot pit a suitable distance away from the other huts. The pit was roofed over with boards, through which holes were cut.

Given these conditions, the question of going home became obsessive. There was no way in which everybody could return together. It had to be done piecemeal. A destroyer could take forty; a submarine ten; a minesweeper just half a dozen. One question had to be settled: who was to sail first?

There were no senior officers present to adjudicate over such a matter. A chief petty officer suggested a solution: 'We'd better go Bolshevik and form a committee.' The committee of twelve established two simple rules: those over forty went first, in alphabetical order; and the others were to put their names in a hat and go home according to chance.

At first every man ached to get out of the hell-hole

of Vaenga. Mike pined for his home in Willis Road, thought mournfully of his mum, envied Martin the luxurious warmth of his Mediterranean posting, and wrote long, misspelt letters to them both detailing his miseries. He was downcast not to be included among the hundred picked for the first return journey with the *Trinidad*, now patched up with the steel plating brought in by the *Edinburgh*. But the *Trinidad*'s fate modified his eagerness to leave. She sailed as Admiral Bonham-Carter's new flagship on 13 May; on 14 May she was bombed and sunk.

Thereafter enemy pressure made the route increasingly hazardous. Hitler ordered the convoys to be stopped permanently. It was now full summer, and the Germans could attack round the clock. Formidable ships, in particular the new battleship *Tirpitz*, struck out from the Norwegian fiords. In July there came the disaster of PQ 17, in which twenty-three of thirty-six ships were lost. Later the same month the minesweeper *Niger* ran into a British minefield which had not found its way on to her charts and went down with forty *Edinburgh* survivors. After these disasters many back at Vaenga wondered whether they wouldn't rather sit out the rest of the war in unhealthy boredom with the Russians rather than risk death in the Arctic.

Mike was one who thought along these lines. He had had one ship blown from under him. He had every intention of surviving. If that meant enduring a few more weeks of hunger, then he was ready for it. He drank the greasy tea, forced down the boiled barley, chewed the dried fish. He held his breath over the foul-smelling sewage. (Once, his wallet slipped from his back pocket while he was squatting over a hole. He persuaded four of his mates to dangle him upside down over the sewage so that he could retrieve it.)

The real problem was the tedium – broken by unnecessary morning parades and mock guard duty with wooden rifles – and ill health. The nearest hospital was in Murmansk. A few of the men had been there to be treated for frostbite. They'd seen a Russian who'd had a leg amputated after being given just two aspirins. After that, those who became ill refused to admit it.

It took Mike three months to get home. He was eventually told that he would be going by train to Archangel, now clear of ice for the summer. He thus became one of the few of the *Edinburgh*'s survivors actually to see Murmansk. By now it was high summer, but the place was still a ghost town. The streets were rubble and mud, lined with the burnt-out shells of houses through which poked the remnants of furniture and iron bedsteads. Ruined concrete blocks nudged up from the chaos of wood and brick. About the only clear area was the railway itself, a single ribbon from the south-east that cut through the ruins and branched out along the dockside. The few inhabitants were unsmiling bureaucrats and officers supervising the labourers who transferred the goods from the convoy ships at the railhead.

The sight of that operation added a new dimension to Mike's experience of Russia. Vaenga had been bad, but at least men ate and lived. On the dockside, men did not eat, and they died. He had never seen people so starved and weak – dead eyes, sunken cheeks black with stubble, scrawny bodies wrapped in rags. They were no longer people, for as convicts condemned to slave labour, to them it no longer mattered whether they lived or died.

As he was waiting on the dockside to board his train, along with a dozen mates, he saw a figure lying stretched out and propped up against some crates. He wandered over with the rest, thinking the man was unconscious. The figure was horribly emaciated and very dead, with a bullet hole through the forehead. At that moment the Russian who was supervising their departure called to them from the wagon to which they had been assigned, then strolled over to see what had caught their attention. It did not seem to occur to him that there was anything odd about the broken figure slumped on the stones. He grinned. 'No work!' he said, putting two fingers to his head by way of explanation. 'Lazy man! Boom, boom!'

The men – all teenagers, but grown men in experience – walked back along the dockside, past the heavy cranes that were used to unload the British and American war materials, to the railhead. The wagon in which they travelled was more like a prison – unsecured benches and no windows, only ventilation holes set high up under the roof. Mike saw nothing of the journey, nor anything of Archangel, where he was embarked on a cruiser, the *Somali*.

He was only a little luckier with the *Somali* than he had been with the *Edinburgh*. She was torpedoed, and broke up in a gale after the crew and passengers were transferred to another vessel. He eventually reached Lock Ewe in north-west Scotland, one of the regular bases for the reception of convoys, on 26 September 1942.

At the Loch Ewe base, Mike was fed, billeted and told to report the following morning to the administration office. There, one of a queue of survivors, one of whom he knew well, he gave the details of his past few weeks, collected back pay, was given dockets allowing him to pick up new kit, told he could take fourteen days' leave, received orders to report back to Chatham after his leave, and was given travel warrants to get him by rail from Inverness to London and from there to Chatham.

He could have made a telephone call home; but his mother didn't have a phone. Besides, he liked the idea of surprising her. In Murmansk he hadn't heard from her, or indeed anyone. He had written home a couple of times, but there was no way to tell her of his final departure. After another day spent eating and sleeping, he joined a small convoy of three naval lorries taking seamen the sixty miles to Inverness.

The last few months had changed him. His body still needed to recover from the Russian food, the hunger, the cold, the lack of sleep. He was gaunt. But he was also tough. He had come through, and was confident, even proud, of it. Mike had a story to tell – everyone wanted to hear about the gold – and was suddenly at one with the men, some of them twice his age, who shared his compartment for the next day and night.

His outward jauntiness reflected an unusual independence of spirit. He was, at heart, a survivor. As a result he found himself confronted with a problem. He had to remain in the Navy; but how could he avoid being sent back on another sodding Arctic convoy? He pondered the question on and off for twenty-four hours, when he wasn't talking, playing cards or sleeping, but failed to find an answer.

He was back at Liverpool Street station early on 1 October. With clean kit, a full belly, money in his pocket and a good night's sleep behind him, he felt on top of the world for the first time in months. Hopping tubes and buses across bomb-torn London, he grinned to himself as he imagined the surprise that would greet his unexpected arrival. 'Gawd!' she'd say. 'We thought you was dead!'

He was prepared for devastation, and so found himself pleasantly surprised. On the home front the worst of the war was over by late 1942 – no more night raids, people fed, wages on the up. Repairs to bombed areas, especially the devastated East End, had not yet got underway and there were the same gaps in the streets that he remembered from his visit at Christmas 1941, for his dad's funeral. But houses had glass in the windows again. Life seemed to be returning to the old place. A few shops were open.

He walked up Willis Road, savouring the moment, and stood in front of his own green front door.

He tried the handle. It was locked. Not surprising – Mum must be down the hospital.

At that moment there came a voice from over the way.

'Is that young Mike?' It was old Mrs Reynolds from number thirty-four, still in curlers, with a scarf over her head.

''Ello, Mrs Reynolds. How's things? Know when Mum'll be back?'

'Cor, Michael, you ain't 'alf grown up!' She gave a tight smile. 'You'd better come on in and 'ave a cup of tea.'

'I could do with one. Ta. But . . . do you know when Mum's goin' to be 'ome?'

She didn't answer, but turned and went back into

her house, leaving the door open. Mike followed her through, down the passage and into her little kitchen.

'Sit down, young Mike,' she said, then pushed a chipped mug towards him and put a pot in the middle of the table. She sat down opposite him. She wasn't smiling any more.

Mike had seen that look before, from the communications officer on the bridge of the *Edinburgh* just after he'd finished talking to Peaches.

'It's Mum, isn't it?' he said.

'Yes, Mike, it is. But it's more than that . . .' Mike stared into his cup. Mrs Reynolds pulled a handkerchief from her apron. 'After your dad was killed, you know, she seemed to pick up quite nicely. She was working in the 'ospital, wasn't she, and never wanted to leave London, like a lot of us. Buggered if old 'Itler was going to scare us lot out.' She smiled through tears. 'Doing a good job, she was, and 'appy with it. Then you went away. We all knew about them convoys and she began to say you wasn't never coming back. Then there was Martin.'

'Martin? I never 'eard nothing about Martin.'

'Don't suppose you did, dear. I wrote to you. Suppose the letter went down at sea. 'Ad you 'eard he was on the *Eagle*, in Gibraltar?'

Mike nodded. Martin had mentioned he was being transferred. The *Eagle* was an aircraft carrier, and was used in the Malta convoys. In August 1942, when Malta was near collapse, the *Eagle* was part of the convoy intended to relieve the island. Code-named Pedestal, the convoy left Gibraltar on 10 August, and was hit hard almost at once. 'The *Eagle* was the first to go,' Mrs Reynolds went on. 'They got off, most of them, almost a thousand, they said. But not Martin. That telegram just about finished your mum.'

Mike put a hand over his eyes. Martin always used to say it was so nice down the Med. He'd looked forward to the *Eagle*, said he wouldn't mind learning to fly come the end of the war. Gibraltar was where Mike had been hoping to go. Now Martin, who'd seemed to have had it so easy, was gone, while he, who'd had such a rough ride, had come through.

Mrs Reynolds blew her nose loudly. 'Then there was the news about the *Edinburgh*. So many times she was in 'ere, crying, over tea, like us lot now, saying there's nothing left – first it was Dad, then Martin, now Mike. It was just at the time when we was beginning to think it was going to be all right. We'd come through the Blitz. There was rationing, but we wasn't starving. We was all doing our bit. But yer mum, she didn't seem to 'ave nothing to live for no more. She just seemed to sort of fade. I went to see 'er down the 'ospital. The doctor said it was TB, spending too many nights down them tube shelters. But I reckon she just died of a broken 'eart.' She dabbed her eyes. 'The funeral was only a couple of weeks ago.'

They sat in silence for several minutes. Then Mrs Reynolds reached over and touched Mike's hand, as it rested beside his mug.

'I'm sorry to be the one to tell you.'

'It's all right, Lil,' he said. It was the first time he had ever called her by her Christian name.

The mood changed. They sipped their tea in silence for a minute or so.

'Thanks for what you did. You was always a good friend to 'er.'

'What you gonna do, Mike?' she said, looking up.

'Ain't nothing left 'ere for me, is there? My family's the Navy now. I'm meant to 'ave fourteen days' leave. But I might as well get down there straight away.'

'No, darlin'. Best stay 'ere for a few days. I've got the key to the 'ouse. Everything's still in there. You'd better clear it out. Council will be wanting it. You can leave anything 'ere you want to.'

He did stay a few days, even though there really wasn't much to clear. A few pieces of furniture. The old beds. Some clothing. Dad's clock. A drawer full of old letters which he began to read but then threw away. Some photographs he gave to Lil, for safe keeping. The rest all fitted comfortably into the back of the lorry old Wallace used for the second-hand furniture.

Five pounds he got: three lives gone and five quid to show for it.

6

Within a week he was back in Chatham, for more training. There were general classes in seamanship, navigation, ship's maintenance and gunnery. For a month, while awaiting posting to another ship, he learnt more than he'd ever learnt before. He grew. He was nearly seventeen, but looked nineteen; he was six foot tall and weighed eleven and a half stone. Studying and the routines of daily life aboard the training ship helped him gradually to come to terms with the loss of his family.

For a time he forgot his worries about the Arctic convoys. Then a chance conversation raised the matter again, and at the same time offered a solution. In a pub one Saturday in late October, while on shore leave, he got into conversation with one of the harbour divers and remembered old Charlie George, the *Edinburgh*'s chief bosun's mate. This man, Thomas Ridler, made a similar impact. He was not big, but compact and strong, and there was a way in which he talked and bore himself, a self-confidence, that both awed and attracted Mike.

Mike asked about diving. Ridler described the life: climbing into rubber suits – 'Clammy death, we call it,' he said with a laugh – donning what he called a 'hard hat' – a copper helmet with an air tube and a lifeline to the surface – the routine work of clearing fouled propellers; finding bits of equipment dropped over the side; checking on damaged hulls. Ridler was also an instructor for the local training school.

'Once they've done their six months,' he said, 'they're attached as diver to any large ship anywhere in the world. Even cruisers have four divers – you ought to know, being on the *Edinburgh* – and larger ships have anything up to six. Then, of course, there's harbour work, wreck clearance, mine clearance.'

'Cor,' said Mike, reminding himself of Peaches and the gold.

'It's good work,' said Ridler, giving Mike an appraising glance. 'Important. Exciting. Besides, you get more money. A penny a day over basic as a second-class diver, fourpence a day as a first-class diver. And that's before you start the diving. An hour's diving will bring in as much as most seamen earn in a day. When you're a diver, young Cox, you're somebody. Don't you forget it.'

That conversation changed Mike's life. A new world opened up before his eyes. Status, money, an escape from the routines of a seaman's life; an adventure in which he could immerse himself, literally and metaphorically. His attention swung back to Ridler, who, his thoughts way ahead, was watching him quizzically.

'How do I . . . ?'

'No room at Chatham for the next month,' said Ridler with a smile. 'But they've got a bigger place down at Devonport. And you mark my words, they're short of people. There's a lot of ships gone down in a lot of harbours. The rate the world is losing them, you could be in work for the rest of your life.'

Along with Mike when he arrived at Devonport on 1 November 1942 were twelve other trainees. As he discovered that first evening aboard, they were a varied bunch. Yet what they had in common was a certain inner hardness, a self-confidence, a physical robustness, a direct glance that would one day give them a natural authority. Some were raw recruits. Some had already had some training in the Marines. A couple had experience as commercial divers, and were destined to move on quickly. In only one case was the self-confidence the product of class. Andy Cunningham was straight out of Harrow and already had his sights set high.

'I wanted to be a diver as soon as I heard of midget submarines. You've heard of them? No? Couple of divers and some explosives. The Italians are jolly good with them, you know. My uncle told me we're going to get our own and really have a go at Jerry.'

Mike, who was the only one of the group who had been on the Arctic convoys, suddenly connected with what Cunningham was saying.

''Ere,' he interjected, putting down his cup of cocoa. 'I was on the *Edinburgh* taking stuff for the Russkies to the Arctic. Them German ships kept on coming out of Norway at us. I remember the chief saying they used to snuggle into the fiords like mice into their 'oles. Only way to get them, 'e said, was if you was a bleedin' fish. That the sort of thing you mean?'

Cunningham looked across at Mike.

'You've hit the nail on the head, old boy. What did you say your name was?'

'Cox. Mike Cox.'

'Well, Cox,' he said, as if his plans were already a certainty. 'That's what I'm going to do.'

Then there was slow but steady Sid Carter, who was what the lads at Chatham used to refer to as an 'ooo-ar', which meant anybody with a country accent, whether from Kent or Cornwall. As it happened, Sid came from Romney Marsh – the Sussex rather than the Kent side. He had grown up in Rye Harbour, at the south of the River Rother, a couple of miles from the ancient hilltop town of Rye. In those days, before the boom in private yachting, Rye Harbour was a remote little community set on the edge of the Marsh, consisting of a single line of houses, a mile from the sea, guarded by a round flint tower surrounded by a flint wall – a ruined Martello tower, built during the Napoleonic Wars. His father had a small fishing boat. Sid had spent his childhood fishing, swimming, cycling the windswept miles to Rye itself, and playing on the tower.

'Built to keep Boney out, as my dad says. May not look much, he says, but it worked, didn't it? Perhaps it will do the same for Hitler,' said Sid, with a slow smile, when he first told Mike about his family. They had slung their hammocks next door to each other after supper the first night and were talking in low voices.

'Why do you want to be a diver, then, Sid?' Mike asked.

'Well.' There was a long pause. Then Sid spoke with a deliberation that suggested, wrongly, stupidity. 'Dad did a bit of it in the last war. He used to say all this bobbing around on the top of the waves was all very well, but it was like being an outsider. He told me once – I must've been thirteen or fourteen, when we were out getting lobsters – it was like being a hunter. Except you never actually get far into the woods. You lurk about on the edge, go in, shoot something and run out again, all in a few minutes. Don't get very much, don't see very much. "Down there," he said, "there's a whole new world we don't know nothing about." Set me thinking, that did.'

Then Mike had told him about his own background. Sid was to become Mike's first real friend, an equal in a way that Peaches had never been, a steadying influence that counteracted Mike's more quicksilver charm and intelligence.

The next day lessons started. There were two instructors. The first was a Lieutenant Coleville, a distant figure who kept himself very much to himself. The other was Eddy Wainwright, a forthright Yorkshireman – like the chief in the *Edinburgh* – in his late thirties, with piercing blue eyes and a bald head. He talked fast, and a lot, tolerating no fools, and soon became the driving force behind Mike's steadily growing involvement in diving. It was he who made absolutely certain that his charges knew the fundamentals of what they were up against, first in the *Tedworth*'s classroom, then on the forty-five-foot diving launch, constantly reinforcing his information with a string of anecdotes.

From him, Mike learnt at first hand, and in double-quick time, all about the problems that confront man in his attempts to work beneath the surface of the sea.

At sea level the pressure of air is a whisker over 14lb per square inch, 2000lb per square foot, something over ten tons in all on the body's thirteen square feet of skin. Only the fact that the pressure is equal outside and inside allows us to be unaware of the weight of air. But in an environment in which the pressure outside is much less (for example, the top of a mountain) or greater (under water) we become painfully aware of the difference. Water weighs a lot more than air, and the deeper you go the more it weighs. For each additional thirty-three feet the diver descends, another atmosphere – 14lb per square inch – is added to the weight of water. When a sperm whale dives a mile below the surface, water exerts more than a ton of pressure on each square inch of its body.

But because living tissue is largely water, and because water itself is incompressible, there is hardly any sensation of pressure on most of the body; only the air spaces – the lungs, the throat, the ears, the nose – register the change. As any trainee diver is told, if you lower a grape to a hundred feet, it will return to the surface unblemished. But if you lower a sealed tobacco tin to the same depth, it will be crushed flat. The air inside is squeezed into a minute percentage of its former space, and the structure of the seemingly solid tin is no match for the weight of water around it. The diver's problem, then, is to ensure that the pressure of air in his lungs equals the varying pressure of the water around him.

In shallow water the principles of diving are obvious enough, and divers have breathed with the help of a variety of diving-bells and helmets for a couple of centuries. But the deeper the dive, the more intractable the problems become.

For one thing, if air is compressed the proportions of its vital constituents change. Most of the air we breathe is nitrogen, a light, normally inert gas. The useful part, the oxygen, is heavier. Nitrogen compresses less easily than oxygen, with the result that if you double the pressure of normal air, the area taken up by oxygen is reduced. At depth air is no longer air as we know it, and any system that delivers breathable gas to divers must take this into account.

Increasing depth leads to another major problem. Under pressure, more gas is forced from the lungs into the tissues and blood. When pressure is reduced again, it escapes, but it may do so with dire consequences for the diver. The deeper the dive, and the longer it lasts, the worse the possible dangers.

It has been known since the seventeenth century that a rapid change from high to lower pressure produces gaseous bubbles in the blood. In the 1870s a French doctor, Paul Bert, explained why. The oxygen is not of immediate concern: the body uses it up chemically. The problem lies with nitrogen. When pressure falls – as a diver rises to the surface – the nitrogen that has been absorbed by the body recombines into bubbles, exactly as bubbles appear in a bottle of a soda water when pressure is released. The amount of gas in the body and the rate at which it turns back into bubbles vary according to the pressure and the speed at which the diver returns to the surface. A gradual return allows the gas to escape naturally. A sudden return brings on decompression sickness, commonly known as 'the bends' because of the agonizing twisting and turning performed by a victim as he or she attempts to deal with the pain. Pain in the joints is the prime symptom. But there are many others: pain in the muscles, fainting, vomiting, deafness, paralysis and eventually – if the nitrogen bubbles reach the brain – death.

One seemingly obvious solution to these problems is to increase the amount of oxygen. Not so: pure oxygen breathed at much more than double normal atmospheric pressure is lethal. There was no alternative (until much later) to nitrogen.

On the basis of Dr Bert's work, the British scientist John Haldane, working from experience, devised tables that related the depth of the diver to the time spent at that depth, and indicated the time needed for decompression. Careful use of the tables enabled compressed-air divers to work safely down to two hundred feet.

Why not deeper? There were, it seemed, practical barriers. One was that at greater depths divers became confused and began to act as if they were drunk. One or two even lost all sense of reality and responded – as if they were on an LSD trip – by tearing off their face masks and drowning. The condition, the cause of which was not known (and even now is poorly understood), was labelled nitrogen narcosis – 'the narcs' in diving parlance – or, in the more poetic French expression, *les raptures des grandes profondeurs* – the rapture of the deep.

Another consideration was that decompression times for great depths stretched out dramatically. To work for a few minutes at three hundred feet a diver would have had to spend many hours decompressing at various stages on his ascent. Time, money and weather would not allow such operations, even if the diver's physiology would.

In theory there were ways of going deeper – by using another lightweight inert gas, helium, instead of nitrogen. But early experiments with helium had shown that it had its own problems, and it was for this reason that Mike Cox's instructor tolerated no fools, and constantly emphasized the importance of going by the book.

'I have seen terrible things, terrible things, lad,' Wainwright told him. 'I've seen people behave dead stupid and cause deaths. I had a mate in my young days, just after the First World War, and he was brought up a bit quick from a hundred and fifty feet. We thought he'd be all right. Went home to supper. Two in the morning: the bends. Dead by breakfast.'

And again: 'You watch out for a blow-up, Cox lad. I was blown up once. Tripped on something. On my face. All the air into my legs. Like a balloon. Hup – legs first – popped up like a bloody cork. Lucky it was shallow water. In deep water you get a burst suit, nasty bends, drowning – Christ knows what. Keep your head up and legs laced, then you'll be all right.'

Mike's first descent passed off without incident. He was to go off the launch into twenty feet of water. It was midwinter, so he had to wear a woollen sweater, long underwear, a woollen hat and a shoulder-pad to take the weight of the metal corslet that held the helmet. The suit – heavy layers of rubber and twill – pulled on over his feet. Then came the 16lb boots. His assistant piled on the corslet, two weights back and front of 50lb each, and finally the helmet itself, the face-plate open for conversation until the descent started. On land the whole thing was an incapacitating suit of armour weighing about 200lb.

Then the petrol-driven compressors started, he clumped on to the ladder and climbed down into the water. Once submerged, he was released from the suit's weight. He experimentally regulated his buoyancy by adjusting the exhaust valve in the right-hand side of his helmet. At the bottom of the rope he stood disoriented in the semi-darkness and silence, hearing only the clicking of the return valve in his helmet and his own laboured breathing, until Wainwright took his hand and began to walk him slowly across the bottom of the harbour.

The breathing was easy, but even at that depth the clammy pressure of the water against the diving suit round the bottom half of his body was peculiar. The time of day had been nicely calculated. While he was down there the tide began to turn. Wainwright showed him how to crouch down against the tide and, later, to crawl in order to make headway against it.

Over the next few weeks he dived twice a day, gradually coming to grips with ever more difficult tasks. He learnt to use the rope signals for communicating with the tender above. One pull on the breast-rope for 'I'm all right'; four pulls on the air pipe for 'Pull me up!'; and a dozen other signs. He had to manipulate a hammer and chisel to cut through a hawser and to hand-saw through a piece of wood attached to a cable.

The work was intensive and demanding. Physically Mike was maturing fast. The food was good, he was getting a lot of exercise and there was a spring-like toughness about him that would have made him extremely attractive to girls – if he'd had a chance to get to know any. There would have been opportunities. They were allowed out into the town and knew the locals, though they were beginning to feel themselves an élite and never developed the competitive swilling of pints common to groups of young men. Andy Cunningham seldom went with them: he had his own social contacts and would occasionally vanish for whole weekends. Family, he would say, or friends. But most of the other lads had girlfriends in the town and happily entertained each other with tales of who had done what to whom and how soon after the first acquaintance, and who offered the best return for time and money invested. But Mike was the youngest, the least experienced, and he felt it, and remained silent.

Andy Cunningham, meanwhile, was full of what he was learning in the family home in Hampshire.

His father had arranged for him to meet a chap called Crabb ('A jolly suitable name for a diver!') who delighted him with stories of what he called 'human torpedoes' in and around Gibraltar.

It seemed that some 'Eye-ties' had been captured by our chaps sitting on a sort of twenty-foot tube driven by batteries and carrying 500lb of high explosives. The idea was to sneak in over nets and between mines and place charges under British ships. In September 1941 a tanker, the *Denby Dale*, had been blasted in this way and in December six members of the Italian navy's special assault unit, the 'Sea Devils', did more damage to the Mediterranean fleet than all the rest of Mussolini's ships had managed in almost two years of war. Dressed in frogmen's suits and riding their three midget submarines with only their heads showing above water, the men sneaked into Alexandria harbour with some British destroyers, laid charges and crippled two battleships, a destroyer and a fuel tanker. The Italians were all captured; but there was no denying their effectiveness. Crabb and another chap had been given the task of protecting the ships in Gibraltar harbour against any more such attacks. They'd picked up another three human torpedoes, preventing them laying any charges.

Now, said Cunningham – and by this time Wainwright had joined the group – we apparently wanted some human torpedoes of our own.

There had already been one operation with the first two-man 'Chariots' in October 1942 against the *Tirpitz*. Two of them were ferried across the North Sea in a small fishing boat and then towed into Trondheim Fiord, where the *Tirpitz*, still the most formidable of the dangers confronting the Arctic convoys, was moored. Only bad weather, which snapped the two lines, prevented the attack. The frogmen escaped through Sweden.

Wainwright bent forward across the mess table.

'Where'd you get all that stuff, Cunningham?' he asked.

'Family, sir, family,' he said airily, as if he were privy to the inmost secrets of the War Cabinet, then conceded: 'Well, a lot of the details are still secret, I suppose.'

He supposed right. There was already a good deal more to small-scale naval operations than he could possibly have known. Army Commandos in the Mediterranean had set up their Special Boat Sections, whose powerful swimmers and expert canoeists had in 1941 recced Italian-occupied Rhodes and mounted raids on ships and coastal installations around the Mediterranean. Success, and the sheer thrill of such pinprick adventures, attracted the attention of David Stirling, the founder of the SAS, whose D Squadron of canoeists inherited the SBS name when Special Services was reorganized after the North African campaign ended in 1942.

At the same time a number of separate special boat

units – canoeists, frogmen, powerful swimmers all – had been trained to mount raids on the coast of occupied Europe. From a medley of commando, SAS, naval and Royal Marine units there would soon emerge the Special Boat Squadron proper, the forerunner of today's Royal Marines' SBS, cutting its teeth in the Mediterranean. But in 1942, when Cox first became aware that there was demand for specialists in marine operations, the sea-based raiders were members of private armies, with no unified command.

It was for one of these specialized units that Wainwright was seeking volunteers. The training camp was way up north where nobody could go nosing about.

'They want four of you chaps as soon as possible. You'll be one,' he said, looking at Cunningham. 'But the rest of you, tomorrow I'll tell you a bit more about being a frogman. Then I want some volunteers.'

The next morning Wainwright told the twelve young divers something about other aspects of diving. He started by explaining that the trouble with the equipment on which Mike and the others had trained was that it was cumbersome and tied the diver to a surface support system. This disadvantage had long been recognized, and for well over a century divers had been experimenting with equipment now generally referred to as 'scuba' – self-contained underwater breathing apparatus.

The first workable scuba was invented in 1825 by an Englishman, William James. In his apparatus a huge belt served as an air reservoir. But the suit was heavy. It had a steel helmet and heavily weighted boots, and was designed for walking on the bottom, not free swimming. In 1865 two French engineers designed a scuba with an air valve that responded to the changes in water pressure and delivered air to the diver's mouthpiece only when he took a breath. But this early scuba gear allowed dives of no longer than a few minutes and no deeper than forty feet.

The length of time a diver could stay down increased to three hours in the late nineteenth century with the invention of the first self-contained oxygen apparatus, though of course it could not be used below thirty-three feet, the depth at which oxygen becomes poisonous. In the 1930s a Frenchman, Yves le Prieur, invented a suit which consisted of a steel cylinder of compressed air connected by an air hose to a full face mask. There was no regulator, however, and much of the air went to waste. Only in 1942 was this feature introduced, when Jacques Cousteau and Emile Gagnan produced their aqualung. Their invention – or rather their novel application of technology that had been in existence for some time – was to revolutionize free diving.

But the aqualung, even if the Allies could have swung into immediate production, was clearly not suitable for cold North Sea waters, which was the

Admiralty's particular concern at the time Wainwright was delivering his lecture. Cunningham's information, he said, was good, except that in the future research would be concentrated not on the Chariots but on a more advanced form of underwater assault vehicles known as 'X-craft'. These midget submarines were later used to launch a partially successful attack on the *Tirpitz* in late 1943.

But all that was only part of what Wainwright had to say.

'If you have been following the news,' he told them, 'you'll know that things aren't looking quite as bad now as they did a year ago.'

Monty had pretty well cleared up in North Africa, he continued. 'No time at all we're going to be in Tripoli. The Yanks are pouring men in. Malta seems to be in the clear. Not long now and they'll be wanting to use North Africa as a jump-off point to invade Italy. There are a lot of ports on the African coast, and Jerry knows they'll be pretty vital to us. Now, Jerry's not stupid. As soon as he pulls out of a port, he does his best to block it. Not just mines, but old ships, tankers, dock gear, concrete – anything he can't get away is blown up and dumped across the harbour mouths. Come the time we want to get in there with some cargo and troop ships, we're likely to have our bottoms opened up. It'd be like running over a lot of tin-openers. All this business about frogmen is all very well, but I've got to get some of you chaps down to North Africa smartish. HMS

Nile – that's the base at Alexandria in case you're wondering – wants divers for the inshore squadron. But from today your training's over. You're divers, whether you feel ready or not. Now, before I tell you what I think, I want volunteers. Questions?'

Mike glanced at Sid Carter.

'You ask him,' said Sid. Mike nodded.

'I like goin' deep,' said Mike. 'How deep can you go with a scuba?'

'Don't know, lad. If you can pressurize the canisters properly, three hundred feet perhaps. Trouble is, if you stay down a long time you have to come up slow, and control it yourself. That takes time. Very dangerous, that. No, if you want depth – useful working depth – you stick to the old hard hat. It's safe as houses if you use it properly.'

'How deep will hard hats go?'

'Depends on the narcs and decompression times. Best dive so far is five hundred feet. But that's a simulated dive in a tank, using helium. We've never talked about that. From that depth it would take bloody hours to decompress – no one knows how long – but at least you've got air and time and you're not expending energy swimming about. You want my guess? In a few years we'll be taking quick trips down to five hundred feet or so.'

'What about a thousand?'

'Only in diving bells and submarines, son. Forget it.'

But Mike knew he would never forget it, and therefore volunteered with Sid for hard-hat work clearing harbours in the Mediterranean.

Just before he went he spent Christmas 1942 with Sid's parents. The two young men had a week's leave, and were given travel warrants that would take them to London and then down to Rye and back again, in time for the New Year. Mike had never in his life been down to the south coast. A couple of summers in the 1930s he'd been taken with other families from the East End down to pick hops near Ashford, but they'd always remained inland, among the shacks and the fields.

Along the coast, the noise of war had receded. The bombing raids had stopped, the doodle-bugs were yet to come. There was no shortage of food, though it was mainly fish. There was beer to drink, and Woodbines to smoke. Mike and Sid walked the windswept beaches, smelt the salty mud of the Rother at low tide, took buses into Rye, wandered through the town's steep, damp, cobbled streets. They made proud contributions to the family budget from their pay packets. They gave, and were given, small presents. They talked and drank with neighbours, and were treated as war heroes. Mike loved it.

It was here, on a windy walk along the shingle, that Mike talked about the *Edinburgh* again. He relived for Sid the arrival of the gold, the loading, the story of the broken box, the torpedoing and the scuttling, the desolation of Vaenga and Murmansk.

'That's why I took to diving,' he confided. 'Weren't any way I was going back on them convoys.'

'Never know,' said Sid, with his slow grin. 'You might be landed back on convoy as a diver. Like your chief.'

The thought had not occurred to Mike.

'Cor, bloody 'ell. I don't want that again.'

There was a pause. They walked on in silence, feet crunching on the shingle, the wind snatching at their clothing.

Then Sid said: 'Perhaps it wouldn't be such a bad idea at that.'

''Ow d'ya make that out?'

'Well, you could go down and fetch the gold.'

'Do what?'

'You're a diver. You just said she went down nice and slow. You know where she lies, don't you? Well, sort of. You know your way around her. You could go down and fetch it up.'

Mike stopped and looked at Sid.

'You know something?' he said. 'That's not a bad idea. 'Ow deep is the Barents Sea?'

'How the hell should I know? Look at a map. We got one at home.'

'All right, then. And if it's shallow, blimey, all you'd need is a bit of good weather and some nice woollies. What do you think, Sid? We could go back there and 'ave a go after we've done for 'Itler.'

It was more than just a joke. They looked at a map. The Barents Sea was shallow, it told them, which in this case meant between two hundred and a thousand feet.

'Too deep, I bet,' said Mike.

'Never know,' Sid replied optimistically. 'Might be possible, mightn't it? Anyway, who knows how deep they'll be diving after the war?'

'Yeah, that's right,' said Mike, going as silent as Peaches had when he heard talk of the gold. 'Yeah.'

Mike and Sid formed part of the crew of a mobile unit that went out to clear wrecks in the Mediterranean in January 1943. First stop, Tripoli, displaying even through its bomb damage the remains of its historic beauty: the great Spanish castle, the massive sea wall, the lines of palms.

On their withdrawal on 23 January 1943 the Germans had done their best to block the harbour with wrecks, including a forty-two-thousand-ton Italian liner, *Giovanni Batisti*. They had also breached the breakwaters and moles that guarded the harbour, to expose it to the open sea. It didn't really delay the Allies for long. Mike and Sid, with no time but to work, eat and sleep in their Nissen-hut barracks, were among those who laid charges to blast a passage through the block-ships. As a result the first supply ships were able to creep into Tripoli's harbour only two weeks after the Germans left.

Shortly after the first boats entered, when work had become more routine, Mike learnt at first hand the truth of what Wainwright had told him a few weeks before: 'Accidents happen, lad, and sometimes there's nought you can do.'

They were anchored outside the harbour. Mike was on the harbour tender and Sid was down below in shallow water – thirty feet. They were off the main approach, investigating a small launch that had probably gone down during the Allied assault a few weeks before. It would never be a danger to shipping, but they had been told to take a look at it in case it contained any information that might be of value. It was a clear day and the water was calm. The outline of the boat appeared, rippling among rocks. Off to one side, the seabed became deeper and darker.

Sid reported over the phone link that the wreck lay near the edge of a shelf.

'I'm standing on the stern,' came Sid's distorted voice over the speaker, above the hammering of the compressor. 'Play out a bit more, Cocky. I'm going to have a look inside.'

Mike allowed several more feet of hose and lifeline to unwind from the drum, but as he was doing so there came a distorted squawk over the intercom: '*Oh God, no!*'

Suddenly the hose began to unravel, accelerating

at a frantic rate. Mike threw the handbrake on to hold the spinning drum. There was a screech of metal, the hose and lifeline snapped taut and the boat lurched. The compressor picked up to a higher level. There came through the speaker a strange, blood-chilling, gargling sound, then silence.

'Sid! Sid! You all right? Sid!' Mike shouted.

There was no reply.

It was only a month later, when he himself went down to see the launch, that he was able to confirm what must have happened.

The launch had been balanced perilously on the edge of the rock and coral shelf that Sid had mentioned. Its stern must either have been overhanging or resisting on a weak outcrop of coral. The extra weight, as Sid had climbed aboard, had unbalanced it. As he entered one of the hatches the boat had tipped. It had begun to slide down the side of the shelf and, as it went, the edge of the hatch into which he was climbing had hooked his pipe and lifeline. The weight of the boat had taken up the slack and jerked many more feet from the supply above. Sid had had no chance to do more than cry out. By the time Mike had reacted, he must have been carried another fifty or sixty feet down into the depths. When the pipe and line suddenly sprang taut, he was jerked up clear of the hatch, while the boat continued its slow plunge down to a hundred and fifty feet, where Mike found it.

Sid would still have been at only a hundred feet,

normally well within any safety margin. But he went down too fast. In a few seconds the sudden increase in weight of water around him added another 20lb per square inch to all parts of his body unprotected by his helmet. His helmet, being circular and made of copper, was well able to withstand the increase in pressure; but the suit below offered no such protection.

A sudden increase in pressure creates a condition known by divers as 'the squeeze'. A small squeeze is not particularly rare, and the results are usually nothing worse than some burst blood vessels in the eyes, and perhaps a bleeding nose.

But a squeeze on the scale of the one experienced by Sid is entirely different. The weight of water pressing on the lower body, outside the protection of the helmet and corslet, suddenly exceeded the helmet's internal pressure by 20lb per square inch, or about six tons in all. Something had to give.

It gave directly upwards, into the helmet, which offered the only place for expansion. Stomach, liver, heart and intestines collapsed into the lungs. These in turn were forced straight up the neck cavity and out through the mouth, nose and ears. Insofar as it was possible in the space available, Sid's body was turned inside out, squeezed like toothpaste into the helmet. That was the frightful sound that Mike had heard through the intercom. He knew – even as his own appalled cry died on his lips – that there was nothing he could do. He knew from the compressor's gauge how far Sid had fallen. His imagination told him the rest. He sat silent and ashen for half a minute. Then he retched over the side of the boat and when there was nothing more to retch he sat trembling with shock while the boat rode the gentle swell.

After ten minutes, his trembling under control, he realized that he would not be able to lift what remained of Sid into the boat. The weight of both corpse and helmet would be over 300lb. In any case he could not have faced the sight of the tight-packed red face-plate. He wound in the pipe until about ten feet dangled below the boat. Then he hauled in the anchor, started the engine and headed slowly back towards the harbour.

He moored at a suitably deep spot by one of the jetties and went off to report.

The men he was working with had seen a good deal of death. Often in the boats they salvaged there were bodies – shattered, eroded, broken bodies. But this was something utterly beyond their experience. It was the stuff of nightmare. Nursing a brandy, Mike explained the circumstances. For the harbour-master, he also explained the necessary effects of being dumped suddenly from thirty to a hundred feet.

'Christ. What the hell do we do?'

'He was me mate and a diver. That's 'ow I want to remember 'im. For all our sakes, don't try and get 'im out of there.'

They made a special coffin for Sid. It was very

wide at the top. They took the weights off his feet, cut the pipe and the lifeline, nailed him up and buried him at sea.

Riding back from the burial in the harbour launch, Mike thought: If that can happen here, in the shallow, calm waters of the Med, what on earth will I need to dive to many times that depth in the icy, windy waters of the Barents Sea? A bit more than some nice warm woollies, that's for sure.

The first Mike knew of the new direction in his career was when the CO called him in and told him he was volunteering for assignment to Cairo.

'Don't ask why, Cox. I can't tell you. But on past experience, if they ask you to volunteer, something's up. So I wouldn't be allowed to tell you even if I knew.'

'They want divers, sir?'

'Christ knows.' The major gave him a bored look and licked his neat little moustache. He was a gin-and-tonic paper-pusher sidelined into admin for the duration, who wrapped boredom around him as a defence against disappointment. 'All I know is, there's a Hercules leaving tomorrow and you're volunteering to be on it. Got it?'

'Sir.'

He had seen little enough of Tripoli, and had high hopes of Cairo. The Nile. Pyramids. Dusky girls behind veils. Except that 'Cairo' turned out to be metaphorical. That was where the orders came from. Mike was destined never to see the place. His Hercules – a rattling empty warehouse of a plane that made conversation with the five cargo handlers quite impossible – landed in Alexandria, after four roaring hours. Assigned a tent, in a city of tents that had become a suburb over the past five years, he was simultaneously told to report to his staff sergeant's office as soon as he was ready.

Still no explanations. A brief shuffling of papers, an abrupt order, and he was off in a jeep out of the camp, through a ramshackle suburb of mud-brick houses into town, to an ornate stone building created at the turn of the century, probably for some imperial administrator or thrusting businessman.

The driver, silent as the Sphinx in face of Mike's tentative questioning, led him up sweeping stone stairs to a first-floor office – where at last he found the answers he had been waiting for.

Behind a huge oak desk sat Andy Cunningham.

'Andy, I mean . . .' he hesitated, suddenly disconcerted, first by Cunningham's smiling confidence in this imposing office and then by the sight of the captain's badge on the hat lying on the edge of the table.

Cunningham grinned. 'Good to see you, Cox.'

Mike smiled back, and felt a burden lift from him. There was much to explain, but he knew some of the story without words. Cunningham was on his way up, and he had chosen Mike to go with him part of the way.

'Quite a job I had prising you loose from those bureaucratic bastards in Tripoli,' said Cunningham. 'Now: at ease, sit and attend.'

For an hour, Mike listened. Cunningham had achieved his immediate ambition, training in special services, undertaking a few cross-Channel operations, and had then been posted to Cairo to help create similar units. He knew Mike was trained as a diver, of course. That might come in useful. But it wasn't just divers they wanted: it was tough young men willing to dive, swim and paddle into action.

The intention was to nip at the weakening flanks of the Third Reich, which still garrisoned a ring of Aegean islands, the outer bulwarks of Germany's Balkan defences. Rhodes, Karpathos, Leros, Kos and half a dozen others harboured several thousand Germans. Increasingly cut off from the collapsing heartland of the Reich by Allied advance in Italy and eastern Europe, the enemy were doing their best to arrange evacuation. It was the job of the SBS, transported by naval motor launches, submarines and locally built caiques, to cut their supply lines, sink their evacuation ships and force their surrender.

'You game, Cox?'

'Yes, sir.'

'Good man. Need a bit of training, of course. Handling a Bren, unarmed combat, canoes, explosives. I think you'll find it an interesting month.'

'Yes, sir. But why me?'

'Two things, really. I've been at this game a couple of years now, and I've seen the truth of what I was told at the start. The key to a successful team and a successful operation is character. Don't ask me to tell you what it is. I just recognize it when I see it. I saw it in you when we first met. Second thing is expertise. You have some pretty unique experience, Cox. It's not that – what do you call it? – "hard-hat" stuff we need. Too much gear. I want frogmen, chaps who can go underwater. I want someone who understands the problems, and someone who can train other chaps.'

'But, sir, I've never . . .'

Cunningham waved an arm impatiently. 'I know, I know. But you know a lot more than most. If I get you the equipment, I want you to test it, use it and train others. Right?'

So it came about that Mike found himself squatting below the open hatch of a sturdy wooden schooner, checking the intake valves on his scuba gear, or rather his Underwater Swimmer's Set Mark 1, as it was officially known: little more than a two-hour oxygen tank, face mask and weights. The schooner, the *Tewfik*, was moored in a bay of Nisiros, an island just off the Turkish coast. As the result of a radio intercept it was known that two small German boats would be calling at the little town, Mandracchio, as part of their routine patrols of smaller ungarrisoned islands.

There were seven men in Mike's group, all but one holed up ashore in the houses of friendly Greeks. He had got to know them well over the past few weeks. Their leader, Major Ian Patterson, an ex-para. Andy Cunningham himself, the Number Two. The Cretan interpreter, Kankakis, who could tell you the story of the islands and their peoples with the fluency, if not refinement, of a Homer. The signaller, Bill Stephenson, who spoke Greek well – far too well to pass as a local. He had been left behind as anchorman, to look after the well-hidden radio and move the boat in case of trouble. And finally there were two marines, both corporals, Geoff King and James Rhodes.

'I spy Jerries.' It was Stephenson's voice, from up above, on deck.

Mike, dressed in lightweight brown trousers, shirt and desert boots, stowed his scuba gear in its canvas bag and stood up warily. Stephenson, sheltering from the midday sun under the shadow of an overarching sail, tilted his square jaw towards the horizon.

There, beyond the point that guarded the parched little houses of Mandracchio, two patrol boats were approaching.

'OK. I'm off,' said Mike.

He knew exactly what he had to do. He had been over the ground, literally and metaphorically, twice. Collect scuba gear, flippers and limpet mines. Down the gangplank, through the shallows and into the scrub. Important to be off the boat in case some officious Jerry came to check. (If he did, he would find only a fishing boat manned by Stephenson acting an innocent Greek from Piraeus.) Then, down between outlying houses, and into the water of the harbour. Swimming easily in order to minimize the trail of air bubbles, Mike would find the shadowy hulls, gently attach the limpet mines, timing them to explode half an hour later, then return the way he had come.

That was his agenda. It was not, however, the main agenda. That was being dictated by Patterson and the others. Their task was to kill the Germans, the sooner the better, rendering Mike's plan unnecessary. But there was no telling in advance how strong the German patrol would be or what they might do. Perhaps they would take over some well-constructed house and settle down for the afternoon and night in safety. Or perhaps they would take a cursory glance and leave at once. So: no chances. Mike had to mine the boats, and ensure no hasty departures.

He learnt what happened in the village later. Even as he was slipping into the disconcertingly limpid water, Kankakis was informed by one of his many friends that the twelve Germans, six from each patrol boat, had arrived with a purpose. In the village was a small orphanage, run by half a dozen nuns. The Germans wanted ten of the children. No one knew why – as hostages, perhaps. On landing, they ordered the children to be ready by early afternoon with any possessions they had.

Time enough for Patterson to act; he was issuing orders even as Mike flippered across the shallow harbour. Then, while his commander and the rest remained in the shed that had become their base camp, Kankakis made his way to the orphanage, reassured the weeping nuns and arranged for the children to be led quietly away into the hills, while their bags were placed outside in the road in apparent readiness for departure. By then, an hour later, Mike was back among the sheltering scrub, his canvas pack empty of limpet mines.

Shortly afterwards the twelve Germans arrived to collect the children. They were met by a priest. This they had not expected; no one had seen a priest, nor had the nuns mentioned one. But it did not remain a puzzle to them long.

The priest, with an expansive gesture, invited the Germans to follow him through the double doors of the orphanage into a courtyard. Forewarned, the nuns stayed clear. Inside, the priest – Patterson, in robes supplied by the nuns through Kankakis – whipped a pistol from beneath his vestments, with a warning shout of '*Hände hoch!*'

The senior German signed his own death warrant by cocking his machine-pistol. A single shot from Patterson's gun took him in the chest. But the action gave others time to raise their weapons, and also warned Patterson's men outside that they should intervene. While Patterson threw himself backwards at the still-open door, King and Rhodes appeared, weapons raised. Then, for a few seconds, there was a pandemonium of firing. Three Germans dropped; several others threw themselves through windows. Most were finished off by other members of the SBS team outside.

The mêlée ended as suddenly as it had started, with three Germans standing open-mouthed, their hands raised.

A quick count: four dead inside, three prisoners, three dead outside. Two missing.

Shouts came from down the hill. Villagers pointed. Then, on the quayside, two figures leapt into one of the patrol boats' dinghies. They were too far for a shot. Patterson could only watch in frustration as they hauled the outboard into life. There seemed to be nothing to stop the men reaching their boats, escaping and summoning help.

Over in the scrub Mike, who had heard the shooting and seen the little figures sprinting down to the quay, looked at his watch and smiled.

The dinghy, its bows raised, was halfway out to the patrol boats, three hundred yards from shore, when the first mine blew, lifting the boat almost clear of the water. Even as it fell back, settling down into a circle of debris like a nesting duck, the dinghy changed course, heading for the remaining boat. It had taken Mike a minute to swim the twenty yards between the two, so the charge would not blow quite yet. With any luck, the men would be aboard when it did.

Clearly the same thought had occurred to them, for the dinghy suddenly veered away and circled the patrol boat warily.

On their second circuit the charge went.

All fell quiet. The dinghy's engine died, leaving the two men sitting glumly, staring at their shattered, sinking vessels.

Mike stood up and waved, first up at the hilltop, where Patterson and his men were still staring down at the scene that had unfolded before them, then down over the scrub behind him, to the schooner, where Stephenson was standing out in the open.

From the quayside there rose a sound seldom heard in the Dodecanese in the past few years: the islanders had emerged from their houses and were applauding.

7

In May 1945, when the war came to an end, Mike had for several months been attached to HMS *Nile*, Alexandria. The focus for SBS operations had shifted to the English Channel, but his expertise was still needed locally, as the major North African ports became depots for supplies from Alexandria, destined for the troops battering their way up Italy.

A strange silence now fell over the two thousand miles of desert coast. All those little places along the North African coast which had become scars in the memories of so many men and families – Alamein, Mersa Matruh, Sidi Barrani, Bardia – sank once more back towards the obscurity from which they had sprung. When silence fell on the Mediterranean, and then across all Europe, Mike expected to be sent home.

But the Navy had other plans for him.

He was called in by the CO and told he had a choice. Either he got shipped home and took severance; or he could review his commission.

'Now,' the CO finished. 'We need chaps like you to go on clearing up around the Med. From Gibraltar to Suez there are enough wrecks, mines and explosives lying about to keep you in work for a lifetime. If you want it.'

Mike had nothing much to get back to. They offered him a five-year contract, assigned initially to a small roving team of divers.

His first mission was in Crete. When the island fell in May 1941 the British lost three light cruisers and six destroyers, and their wrecked remains had to be inspected to make sure they were not a danger to shipping.

Mike and his small team of four divers flew in from Alexandria in June 1945, over the gnarled mountains and rock-bound northern coast to Khania. It was not an inspiring introduction to Crete, for the hills were already burnt brown by the summer sun, and sand-filled wind was gusting up from Libya. They were based in Suda Bay, where the listing hulk of the cruiser *York* lay.

Crete and the Cretans were steeped in war. Hawk-eyed, stubble-jawed men welcomed him with wine and told him, in eager, stumbling English, local details of operations that were already the stuff of legend: here your Colonel Laycock landed commandos; in this tavern General Freyberg drank; along this road, your men withdrew; on that beach they left this or that ship; on such and such a mountain five New Zealanders lived for four years undetected by the Germans . . .

As the wrecks were cleared and the damage was repaired Mike began to see another, deeper side to Crete's character, and came to love it. Along the northern road westwards beyond the Akrotiri Peninsula, and eastward to Heraklion and Mirabella, he found smoky little tavernas patronized by fishermen and sailors. There was one place in particular, a taverna in a little village beyond Mirabella, a place with sawdust on the stone floor. Here, in the cool of the evening, bronzed men in moustaches slammed down cards on bare wooden tables and, as the radio blared out bouzouki music, fishermen did their strange, slow-motion twirling dances, snapping their fingers in trance-like concentration. Mike acquired a taste for retsina, ouzo and all things Greek.

On his trips he began to realize something of the emotional impact of war. He had seen only a few months of action, but these people had lived war for years, and their relief overflowed on to him. At every visit there were gifts of eggs, cakes, oranges, lemons and vegetables. A tiny Charlie Chaplin-like grocer, with a shop that smelt of sweat and garlic, and a wife who was as gnarled and solid as the mountainous spine of the island, greeted him with a free glass of wine every time he came.

It was from the grocer, Petros, that he learnt about the hidden wealth of the Mediterranean and about the sponge fishermen; and thus took another turn in the long road that would many years later lead him back to the *Edinburgh*.

'You a diver,' Petros said one day, pushing a glass of rough red wine across the table towards Mike. 'You know about boats wrecked in war. But we have many, many wrecked boats. Very, very old. Fishermen, they know where wrecks are. They have many, many treasures. Sometimes fishermen pull up a pot in a fishing net. Maybe something in pot. I have a nephew, Marolis, who is fisherman. Perhaps we ask him where wreck is, no? Perhaps you take your boat and go down, look at wreck?'

Mike took up the old man's offer, and one Sunday in September he and one of the other divers borrowed the diving launch for the day – for the channels of Suda Bay were now well marked, and the place was re-established as a working base – and took Petros and young Marolis to a certain spot off Cape Spatha. There they anchored.

The wreck lay in eighty feet of water. Marolis knew it was there because he'd once picked up a double-handled pot, an amphora, in one of his nets. He'd noted the spot and then poured olive oil on the waves, an old trick roughly equivalent to using a glass-bottomed bucket. Through the oil he had seen the shadowy shape of the wreck as defined by the pots. There were hundreds of them. They lay out of reach of any surface motion, little disturbed by currents or tides.

Mike went down to survey his first ancient wreck. It was a trading vessel that must have sunk three thousand years ago. The amphorae were of little interest to Mike. A lot were clearly empty. Others were stoppered, and probably contained what had once been oil or wine. Scores were broken. Beside one of them was a pile of what looked like coral. Mike edged his way around the wreck, kicking up silt with his heavy boot. He bent down and knocked at the coral with his hand, then kicked it. He picked up the piece he broke off. Embedded within it were round, dark slabs.

Coins.

It was his first indication that there might be more to diving in the Mediterranean than drawing cash every week from the paymaster.

They returned to their wreck several times, until it became clear that it was going to make nobody's fortune. They came away from their weekend jaunts with several dozen bronze coins each, most of them heavily corroded. These were judged to be of no great commercial value.

But if there were many other wrecks to be explored, what might not be found with time, money and information?

'We know not much about wrecks here,' said Petros. 'We do not dive here. Only fish. To find wrecks, you must talk to divers. Sponge divers. They know.'

'Where do I find sponge divers, Petros?'

'Not here. You must go to Piraeus. That is where the sponge divers drink and talk.'

For two years Mike worked in Crete, with regular trips to Malta and other harbours. Slowly the war-stricken ports returned to peacetime normality. In Crete, British officials arrived, mostly to arrange payments to those islanders who could prove that they had been part of the resistance. United Nations personnel came to rebuild roads and restore the economy. The more dangerous wrecks were broken up. The Greek Navy returned to Suda. Khania reclaimed some of its former dignity and quaintness. The first tourists arrived, and in Heraklion the first new hotel went up.

Mike had long since left all traces of boyhood behind him. A seal was set on his maturity in another way as well. It was about time: he was twenty-one, but his only experience of sex had been with one of the girls in the local brothel. His mates had cajoled him into a visit, set him up with Angela and pushed him off to her room with ribald laughter.

'What about – you know – VD?'

'Don't you worry about that. She's clean. She's been fucked by every British doctor in Crete.'

She, seeing his boyish uncertainty, had been all admiring glances as he undressed. In bed she seemed excited by his inexperience, guiding his hands to her breasts, pressing with her hips, helping him into her. It was over very quickly, and her interest seemed to him more professional than personal. After facing the whistles of his mates at the bar, and then worrying about the clap, he decided he would not seek out Angela again.

He was on the beach at Agia Pelagia, where he had gone by rattling bus from Suda. The wife of an American UN official who was away in Athens, she was a New Yorker, a sophisticate of thirty-five, beautiful, with dark, loose curls and brown eyes. She was also very bored. He had been sitting on a towel watching her. She was wearing a light-blue swimsuit that contrasted nicely with her well-browned skin. She was used to such glances and decided to take advantage. From the edge of the breakers she caught his eye and gave him a sparkling smile. Her gaze was frank and alluring.

'Hi,' she said. 'You must be with the UN too.'

He shook his head and grinned, about to speak.

'No? Let me guess. You're not Greek, and you don't look American. So you're . . . English, right?' She fetched her towel and spread it beside him, as if it was the most natural thing in the world.

He decided he liked the game and merely nodded, still smiling, not moving.

'Ah-ha. My name's Louise Harling. Uh-uh,' she said, wagging a finger. 'We'll get to yours in a minute. Let me guess more. Young, good-looking, well-built.' Her eyes ran down his limbs. 'Forces, yes? Now which, I wonder? What are you guys up to here? Too young for top brass, too independent, I'd guess, for a regular Tommy . . .'

By the time she had pinned him down he wanted her, and she knew it, and was glad.

He saw her just three times. She was experienced, and a good organizer. Her husband was away for three weeks. She took him back to the hotel, brushed close to him on the stairs, told him a number of extremely exciting things about his body, explained her situation and the rules, then took him to bed.

Over the following two weeks the pattern repeated itself. Each session lasted the afternoon and the evening, during which time they never left the hotel room. Louise proved a good teacher and Mike an avid pupil. At the end of the adventure she pronounced him a perfect lover, took him to the bus depot in the UN car and then drove on to the airport to collect her husband.

In another way, too, his experience expanded. Although still not twenty-two, he was now a man of some status. He was a Diver First Class. Everyone knew about him and the *Edinburgh*. He had a certain reputation even among the senior officers and officials at Suda Bay. He had even told the story of his local wreck to a few people. On one occasion he was accosted by a US government employee whose task was apparently to help assess the level of the next year's government aid programme. Mike had talked freely enough about his work – there was nothing secret about it – and finally, at the

American's request, about his wreck and the coins. The American asked to see them. Mike took them to him. Up until that point he'd no notion that the finds might have a wider significance. The man disabused him on two counts.

'One: I'll buy all twenty off you,' he said. 'I'll offer you $200. I think I know a museum in the States that will be very interested in them. Two: you know the Greeks have laws against robbing wrecks? Anything you do now you'll probably get away with if you keep quiet about it. But they have a point, and things are going to get tougher. Just a word of warning.'

8

In the summer of 1948 he had home leave due, and took it. Already he was beginning to know what he wanted in life. He wanted to dive, and go on diving, and do it better, and go deeper, for longer periods. That's what he would have to do if he was to find treasure. And there was treasure, that he knew. Why, on his way to London, he had broken his flight in Athens and seen in the National Museum a glorious, life-size bronze statue of a javelin thrower which had been found, the plaque told him, in 1927 by a sponge diver clearing a trawler's net.

To live such a life he needed independence, both technical and financial. He wanted the freedom of the depths, an idea first suggested by Andy Cunningham's talk of frogmen. Since then things had moved on. Jacques Cousteau's aqualung was on the market, and free-swimming scuba divers had reached three hundred feet – though a Frenchman who had reached three hundred and ninety-seven feet the previous year died of the bends.

Very well, then. Here were the priorities: the wrecks, for which it seemed he would need the sponge divers; money; equipment; experience . . . and then, in years to come, the *Edinburgh*.

In London he stayed with Mrs Reynolds and gathered all the information he could. He bought his first set of frogmen's fins. He joined the Underwater Explorers' Club. He read everything he could find on diving. He found a well-thumbed copy of the diver's bible, Sir Robert Davis's *Deep Diving and Submarine Operations*.

Other divers he met through the club told him about helium, a possibly safer substitute for nitrogen. It was all imported from the States, apparently, and horribly expensive, but seemed to avoid the narcs and cut decompression times.

He heard how, just before his arrival back in England, in late August 1948, a diver called William Bollard had gone down to five hundred and forty feet off Tarbert, Loch Fyne, on the west coast of Scotland (not far from Greenock, where he'd joined the *Edinburgh* what seemed like several lifetimes ago). It had taken Bollard, breathing a mixture of helium and oxygen, eight and a half hours to decompress – expensive and slow, but at least he'd shown it was possible to beat the bends from over five hundred feet. As Sid might have said, who knew? Could be the *Edinburgh* lay in water not much deeper.

* * *

Mike had to wait another year before he could extend his own range, for 1949 was the first year after the war that the waters off Africa were open to divers. In April, the beginning of the sponge-diving season, his mind set on his future, he arranged two weeks' leave and went to Piraeus, where he rented a room. It was above a café on the front of the charming little fishing suburb of Microlimano.

The single window overlooked the harbour. On the tiled floor, in the far corner, was the bed, low and solid. In the middle of the room stood a small wooden table and a couple of chairs. On one wall was a small brick fireplace. There was a tap, with cold water only, outside his room. Beside the fire, on the floor, was a huge porcelain wash-basin. On a shelf above the small brick fireplace stood a coffee pot and some cups.

The place was not far from the café in which the sponge divers traditionally gathered. The Navarinon, like so many other cafés on the Akti Miaouli, Piraeus's main street, was a single large room with marble-topped tables. Outside was an old cripple, gnarled as a walnut, who shone shoes. Only later did Mike make his acquaintance and learn his story.

Mike spent several days sipping coffees and beers in the Navarinon, overhearing the conversations, which he could now understand quite well. He became known and was greeted by the owner, Sophocles, and the regular customers.

By the end of the week he had struck up an acquaintance with the captain of a sponge-diving boat, one who spoke a little English. His name was Niko Kypriano, a large, welcoming, generous man with a black moustache. He was old enough to be Mike's father. When Mike spoke of his work Niko adopted him immediately. He bought him wine and called him Mikis.

Niko said he came from the island of Kalymnos, like so many sponge divers, and was leaving soon with five relatives to spend several weeks diving. Would Mikis like to come along?

He couldn't, not for any length of time anyway. But perhaps a few days, if at the end he could be taken to a ferry from a nearby island.

'My friend! My son! You come! Tomorrow, eh? You say when we drop you. OK?'

Down in the harbour, Niko showed Mike his boat, the *Hecate*. It was a fine example of the *aktarmardes*, the sponge boats that are modified versions of the double-ended fishing boats common in the Aegean. The sponge boats, thirty to forty-five feet long, were fuller in the beam and had higher bows than the ordinary fishing vessels. With a stubbly little mast set way up in the bows, and room enough below decks to sleep half a dozen people, Niko's boat looked ideal for Mike's purpose.

His commercial timing was fortunate, for sponge diving was already in decline, for several reasons. Accessible beds were becoming fished out; artificial sponges were beginning to appear; and it was a very dangerous occupation.

For centuries the sponges, which in shallow waters were harvested by long poles, were gathered in deeper water by naked divers attached by a lifeline and weighed down with 30lb stones, which also had a line to them. On reaching the bottom the diver would drop his stone, pick sponges for about half a minute and stuff them into a basket. Both the diver and his stone would then be hauled to the surface. By this method experienced divers could harvest sponges from over a hundred feet. The ropes were vital, for below sixty feet the air in the lungs is so compressed by the weight of water that a diver loses buoyancy.

But if traditional methods of sponge diving were dangerous, the occupation became much more hazardous with the advent of helmets in the late 1960s. The principles should have been precisely the same as those that guided Mike's work. But the divers had no idea of the theories of diving safety. For two generations almost every family suffered the loss of at least one of its male members. There was scarcely a diver who didn't know the ghastly effects of decompression sickness. Rather as in remote Welsh mining villages, the suffering and death were accepted philosophically as an inevitable fact of the chosen way of life. Even after the war, one in twenty of the Greek sponge divers was either killed or crippled every year, for few of them knew of, let alone applied, Haldane's decompression tables. In sponge-diving communities a common sight was former divers with swollen joints and wasted limbs, the result of paralysis brought on by a severe attack of the bends. One such was the crippled shoe-shine man outside the Navarinon.

Only wealth could justify such suffering. And from 1950 onwards the returns declined.

Within a day of departure Mike was inducted into the ancient rituals of sponge diving. There was the captain, Niko, the tender – who was responsible for the divers on the bottom and for the equipment – a seaman, an engineer and four divers. It took a day to get to the sponge beds of Kalymons. The next day Mike sunbathed and observed. On the third day he was allowed to use one of the ancient hard hats and gather some sponges himself.

The *Hecate*'s equipment was ancient. The compressors were worked by hand. There was no phone link. For the first time in years he had to communicate by jerking his lifeline and air pipe. But in shallow water it could be safe enough. The water was wonderfully clear. Even though it needed sharp eyes to see the slight irregularity in the waving eel grass that indicated the presence of a sponge, Mike gathered half a dozen. Yes, the *Hecate* would do very nicely indeed.

After half an hour or so he felt three jerks on his lifeline, and was wound up to the surface. He stepped on to the ladder that had been placed over the side for him and tossed aboard his meagre bag of sponges. When his tender undid his face-plate, he got a round of applause.

That afternoon he began to speak to Niko of his long-term plans. He needed a boat, he said, though not necessarily during the sponging season. He needed a captain who knew both the islands and the seabed. If possible, he should speak English. And he needed diving gear, which he might well be in a position to replace later with more up-to-date equipment that would be safer and allow work at greater depths. He said he wished to spend a summer looking for wrecks on the seabed. Finally, if Niko was agreeable, perhaps he would agree to consider going into business with him next year.

'These treasures,' Niko said. 'You can sell them?'

Mike remembered the Americans on Crete. And there were more foreigners in Greece every summer.

'Yes,' he said. 'I can sell them.'

Niko grinned and slapped Mike on the shoulder.

'You come to Piraeus next year. I look out for you at this time, yes?'

They shook hands on it.

In April of the following year, 1950, Mike was back in Piraeus. He had fulfilled his five-year contract. He was twenty-four, in the peak of physical condition, an expert in his profession, with a good knowledge of many of the harbours of the Mediterranean, and driven by ambition. He wanted to be rich: first to enjoy life, secondly to exploit his professional skills to the utmost. All around him now were signs of wealth, mainly foreign wealth: holiday homes (either new or converted from once worthless peasant houses), yachts, restaurants, tourists. He wanted all that, of course, but only to achieve his ambition. He was between two worlds, Greece and Cockney London; the first he could never fully enter, while the second he had left behind. The only world that could be completely his was that of professional diving. That, after all, was the only way he would ever get back to the *Edinburgh*.

Back in the Navarinon, he was no longer the outsider. Arriving early enough in the season to rent his old room again, he settled down to look out for Niko, ready to wait anything up to a week.

The second evening, after he'd enjoyed a light seafood supper, with his customary wine, his life was changed yet again.

Into the noisy, smoke-filled room swept four girls, in full plumage, and as out of place as a hard hat in the Ritz.

All of them wore fashionable, three-quarter-length skirts. Three wore soft jerseys and neck scarves; the other wore a fawn-coloured coat. The place fell silent upon their entry, and their talk was easy to overhear. One was clearly Greek: she asked for a table. The other three, with little exclamations and laughs, revealed themselves as French, English and American. They were nervous, for Piraeus, being a dock area, is not a salubrious place for unescorted young ladies; but equally they seemed set on their course and felt collectively strong enough to put a bold face on their behaviour.

In order not to seem cowed, they began to talk, loudly, inconsequentially.

'My! Is it OK to be here? It seems so, you know . . .' said the American girl. She was the one with the coat. The others laughed.

'Oh, it's fine, fine,' said the Greek girl, brushing back a tumble of dark curls with her hand. 'I look after you. No worry.'

Sophocles, nodding slowly and smiling, indicated a table for four. He caught Mike's eye and frowned as if in warning. Mike grinned and spread his hands, as if to say: 'What do you think I am?'

The girls had class, no doubt about it. But they were no more than schoolgirls. Two – the French and English ones – couldn't have been more than sixteen. The Greek girl, perhaps because she was in control and spoke the language, seemed a little older.

But it was the American who seized Mike's interest. She had a glorious face: a classic jaw line, a few freckles, a mouth that turned up at the corners in a way that gave her a permanently amused expression. Her hair was blonde and pulled back into a bun. She wore no make-up, and needed none. In contrast to the colour of her hair, her eyes were a lustrous brown.

As they all sat down she began to take off her coat, with Sophocles in attendance, and Mike could now see that she had a startling figure. She was wearing a white blouse with a large collar buttoned up to the neck. As her hands went behind her back to slip off her coat sleeves, she raised her eyes and caught Mike's gaze. In that instant he knew he couldn't possibly let her leave without speaking to her.

Sophocles brought retsina to their table. The Greek girl looked at the menu. The American girl caught Mike's eye again. He grinned and raised his glass to her. From the security of her group she smiled back at him quickly, glanced away, stared unseeing at the grubby menu, then looked at him again.

He took his glass across to her table.

'Excuse me, ladies,' he said. 'That's the first time I've ever 'eard English 'ere. I thought I might interpret what's on offer for you.'

There was a slight, uncertain pause before the Greek girl took the initiative.

'You know this place?' she said. 'What is good?'

'First of all, ignore the menu. Sophocles can't spell, 'e can hardly write, but 'e can cook. Sophocles!'

Mike indicated a chair to Sophocles, who made wide eyes at him across the bar and brought one.

Mike then introduced himself. They told him

their names: Joanna, Marie, Helen and Sandra – Alexandra Krassnik. He knew Joanna's type, all right: toffee-nosed. He at once set himself outside her upper-crust English world by saying, as Sophocles brought bread and taramasalata: 'So what am I doin' 'ere, so far from 'ome? Well, I don't normally tell no one, but I'm looking for sunken treasure.' He grinned at their disbelief. 'No, honest. Listen.'

And then he began to tell his story, only breaking off to order, varying the tone with anecdotes: the warmth and poverty of home life, the epic drama of the *Edinburgh*, the wonder of diving, the horror of Sid's death, the infinite possibilities in his own adventurous present and future.

He talked for half an hour, often directly to the American girl, whose stare was the most riveting he'd experienced since Louise; and in all that time, none of the girls uttered a word. It was a masterly performance and it worked. At the end they knew him, and had confidence.

Along the way he asked about them. He'd been right. They were all classy bits, all privately educated, all pals together at a finishing school in Switzerland. They had come down to stay at Helen's home for the Easter holidays. They had said they were going out for a meal locally and then, for a jaunt, decided to slum it down at the docks.

Sandra began to talk. It turned out that her father was in business on his own account and was obviously successful. He had connections in the Middle East, though Sandra didn't know what. He'd be arriving to pick her up in the next few days. Bad news, that, Mike thought. He had no time to waste.

He needn't have worried. Had he been able to analyse why Sandra talked, he would have seen that it was the only way she could cope with the confusion aroused in her by his bronzed good looks and his unwavering attention.

Towards the end of the meal, over coffee, Mike found an excuse for further contact.

'Let me write down where you live,' he said.

Then there was the business of finding a pencil and paper from Sophocles, and the polite ritual of writing down *all* their names. Then he tore the paper in half, wrote down his own name and address and handed the scrap of paper to Sandra. He looked her full in the eye.

'You never know,' he said. 'You might be down this way again.'

As the girls rose to pay, each contributing her share, Sandra went across to get her coat from the stand beside the door.

Mike saw his opportunity. 'I'll 'elp you,' he said, and then, as he held the coat for her, he added from behind: ''Ow about showing you the town tomorrow?' She was breathing fast.

'That would be really nice.'

'Come to my room any time in the morning. OK?'

'I'll try.'

'I'll wait, however long it takes you.'

Mike hadn't asked, or thought, how she was supposed to travel. As it happened, she had enough money on her, and – with the help of her friends – enough freedom, to take a cab from Helen's parents' villa, eight miles away. He heard the cab pull up, and glanced out, as he'd done at the sound of many previous cars that morning. He saw her fumble briefly in the handbag slung over her shoulder. She paid the driver and looked around anxiously for some clue that she was in the right place. Mike leant out of the window. 'Oi!' he called, grinning.

She was wearing the same coat she had had on the previous evening, over a polo-neck jersey. Her skirt, tight-waisted and full, was saffron. A spring flower. A daffodil.

She looked up. Her hair was scraped back off her face, as before, but this time it was hanging in a pony-tail. There was no hint of puppy fat to disguise the perfection of her chin line. She was not yet fully aware of it, but she had arrived early in life at a startling peak of beauty.

'Oh, swell!' she said. 'I didn't know if I'd find you!'

'You want to know something?' he said, grinning down at her as she reached his side of the street. 'You are the most gorgeous girl in the 'ole bloody world.'

She smiled radiantly and curtsied.

'Why, thank you, sir. But you've no need to swear, you know.'

He put on an overdone Oxford accent.

'Oh, gosh,' he said. 'I'm *fright*fully sorry.'

'That's quite all right. Now: am I to stand here *all* day?' She put her hands on her hips and frowned up at him.

He came down the rickety stairs to greet her.

It was as obvious as anything could be that they would become lovers sooner or later. It was only a matter of timing. Mike stretched out his hand to lead her along the little corridor to his room. She put her hand in his.

At the bottom of the stairs Mike paused and breathed in, about to say something. She bumped up against him and one breast lightly touched his forearm. She bent her head minutely towards him as if in preparation for whatever it was he was about to say. The impressions that poured into him were wonderful – warmth, acceptance, desire, the perfume she had put on that morning, the shampoo with which she had washed her hair, the softness of her jersey and her skin, the touch of her breast. All of this Mike sensed so rapidly that he was not consciously aware of most of it. He noticed her hand, her breast, her perfume. The rest of it slapped him in the unconscious, with instantaneous effect. All over his body nerves and cells saluted. Such responses are seldom one-sided.

The effect on Sandra was similar, and as deep and as inexpressible.

'I live upstairs,' he said.

'Gee!' she said brightly, in mock amazement. 'I'd never have guessed.'

There were, of course, all sorts of games to be played before contact. It wouldn't be easy: after all, she was only seventeen. Mike, as usual, was light, easy, charming and funny. Sandra, who might have been decorous and restrained in other circumstances, relaxed and talked about her last few days, which were also her first, in Athens. Wasn't the bomb damage awful, but weren't the Greeks such lovely people; wasn't the civil war just awful, and wasn't he glad that the Reds had been defeated; and wasn't it just fabulous that Helen's house had survived unscathed?

Mike offered coffee. Sandra accepted. He made her laugh by shouting an order out of the window to the café below. He went to get the coffee. By the time they had drunk it, it was lunchtime.

They ate downstairs and Mike, the expert, lectured her about Greek menus, for it was only her second meal in a Greek restaurant. Like the Navarinon, it was a small place, purely local in atmosphere. The air smelt of the firm yellow cheese, *kefelotiri*, that the Greeks use on spaghetti. They ate *tsatsiki*, a cold blend of yoghurt, chopped cucumber and minced garlic. Mike warned her about the garlic, then added: 'But it's OK if we both 'ave it.'

She glanced up and their eyes met. She'd instantly read significance into the remark.

Then there was kebab, and some red wine, while she talked more about her home life. There was a small apartment in Washington that was just for Daddy, the family apartment on Park Avenue in Manhattan, the house near Greenwich, Connecticut, with the tennis court and the horses, the private school not far from there and, inevitably, the finishing school in Switzerland.

In all of this she had been protected from the real world. She knew no single man who had fought in the war, even as an officer. Some of her father's friends had been in the government, but that was about as close as she had got. Her father made money at business, and art and politics, but he had never told her the details. He was often in Washington, and he'd made a lot of money, which was really swell – that was a word she liked – because he had come over from Yugoslavia with Oma and Opa absolutely without a penny in the world in 1920. She didn't even know his history very well, but she knew that by the time he was twenty-one he had made enough money to take care of Mommie. And Mommie's family, wow! you should see *their* place in Boston!

Mike had never been to the States, and the names meant nothing to him, but he loved to hear Sandra talk. She felt the same way about him. An American would have seen in her the immature product of driving ambition married to social status, with a good deal of wealth on both sides. A social-climbing Englishman would have seen in Mike an uneducated but clever adventurer, somebody who would have to achieve by guile and force of personality what would never have been his by birth and upbringing. As it was, each saw the other with no burden of prejudice.

As they went back to his room that afternoon after lunch, Mike again offered his hand to guide her along the little passageway. Recognizing the pattern of events, she again accepted it. At the bottom of the stairs he paused, and she, smiling and expecting another unnecessary comment, bent forward as she had done that morning.

This time, however, instead of dropping his hand down by her side, he put it around her waist and guided her whole body gently up against his. They melted together. Uncertain of what to do next, she remained for a second with her hand against his shoulder, taking short little breaths. He lowered his head and kissed her lightly beneath the ear. As she breathed out, she clasped the back of his neck.

'I wanted to do that this morning,' he said.

'I wanted you to.'

He took her upstairs and guided her to the bed. There were still inhibitions to be overcome, for it was still, after all, only 1950. She was young and a virgin. She hadn't had her body very long, so it would have been surprising if she had been willing to give it all away at once.

Still, she gave a good deal of it away. No clothes were taken off, but there was a lot of kissing and fondling. Her breasts were firmly encased in an uplift bra, and remained that way. But her skirt was full, so that it easily slid up under the insistent pressure of Mike's thigh. He spend most of the afternoon moving on top of her, going through all the motions of lovemaking, ensuring the pressure applied through the security of the clothing was put to the best possible effect. Conversation halted. Her responses became so urgent that Mike, despite his experience, was twice brought to orgasm, and the second time she too vanished into a world of her own, giving hard gasps of pleasure. After that they both became calmer.

'You must be very experienced,' she said.

'No. It's a lonely life, really.'

'But some.'

'A few.'

He told her about the American woman, Louise. She told him she was a virgin ('Daddy's very protective'). She asked, at first tentatively and then more probingly, about sex. He was the first man she'd ever talked to about it. He began to treat her much as Louise had treated him on Crete. He even explained his own responses.

'Golly,' she said. 'Is that what happened? Boys

have tried that sort of thing on me before, but I never realized what they got out of it.'

Then he explained about her reactions, and it was the first piece of sexual instruction about her own body she had ever had.

'Golly!' she said eventually. 'That's why it's so beautiful!'

He kissed her again, then put his hand on her stomach and between her legs.

'So when do we go to bed?' he said.

She looked at her watch. 'Oh, my! Is that really the time? I have to go. I really have to go. I'm terribly late. They'll start sending out search parties and things. And *look* at my dress! they'll all know . . . Oh, golly!'

'Tomorrow. You've got to come tomorrow,' said Mike, as he saw her into a taxi.

'OK, I'll try. I'll really try.'

That evening Niko turned up at the Navarinon.

'Mikis! My son!' he said, holding Mike by the shoulders and kissing him on the cheek.

'How are you, you old sod? Glad to see you!'

As they ate moussaka and drank retsina, Niko told Mike of the previous season's sponge diving. The sponges were good enough to buy petrol-driven compressors. But not as good as before the war. They had been away from Kalymnos for many weeks. There had been problems. The sponges, some of the diving boats, they hadn't done so well last year. Too many boats, not enough sponges. Divers had to go too deep. Some would not be coming back this year. The young boy, Panyotis, the silly boy, was one. When they brought him on deck there had been pain, first in the joints, then in the head, and now he could not walk very well.

'What did he want to do that for, Niko? I told you about the bends, and why it happens. After a long time down, they have to come up nice and slow.'

Niko shrugged.

'I know, Mikis, I know. But the others, it is hard to make them understand. There was a breeze coming, the sun was going down . . . the men were tired.' He sighed. 'These sponges, I ask myself, how long will these sponges last? I have seen sponges, even here in Piraeus, made of rubber and plastic, by machines. We suffer and die for sponges, our wives and daughters weep, and then come sponges from machines. Is this justice? Is this the will of God?' He shrugged again. 'Perhaps our time is past. I am thinking, perhaps I try one more year, then perhaps we do what you say, eh?'

Mike couldn't have put things better himself. He would never have dreamt that Niko would have come round so soon. After all, there was surely still money to be made out of sponges if the equipment was right, and if the divers knew what they were up to. He narrowed his eyes and looked at his friend over the top of his glass.

'Come on, Niko. What's up? You know all the

risks, and you've lived with them for years. There are still sponges down there. You've got the equipment. You can always find people to dive for you. There's more to this story. Got to be.'

Niko grinned, reached across the table, slapped him on the upper arm and seized the bottle. He seemed delighted that his bluff had been called. Clearly there was more, and he was aching to tell.

'Mikis, Mikis, you know me already too well! Yes, there is more. But . . .' He leant across the table and lowered his voice conspiratorially. 'It is very . . .' Then he raised his hand and waggled it to signify infinite mystery, winked and laid his index finger along the side of his nose. 'We go to your room?'

It was a ham-fisted piece of play-acting, but it worked: Mike was intrigued. They paid and left at once. In Mike's room, still clasping the bottle of wine, Niko told his story.

He had taken Mike's offer seriously. He, too, had dreams of wealth. He had asked about ancient wrecks among the sponge divers of Kalymnos, and among the divers from many other islands. He had learnt of many wrecks, and one in particular off Mikonos, in water too deep to be easily reached. No sponges grew there, but the wreck was big, with many amphorae, and might contain many things. He had been told the location. He had found the place. He had sent young Panyotis below. In two dives Panyotis had wandered about the ocean floor, one hundred and eighty feet below the surface, without finding a single sponge. But he had found the wreck, outlined in seaweed and coral and containing hundreds of amphorae. He had seen the arm of a statue. He had knocked off a piece of coral and found two coins – gold coins.

'That was when we had to bring him up, and he come up too fast. Poor boy. But perhaps it is for the best. Now he will stay with his mother. Anyway, he not like down there. Very dangerous place, he say. Boat on edge of steep, steep hill.'

Niko fished in his pocket, drew out his hand and threw on to the table between them two irregular, flattened lumps of metal. They shone a dull yellow. Both coins were clear on one side, and on the other bore the battered but still recognizable features of a woman in profile, wearing a headband, pendant earrings and a necklace. Later, when Mike had identified the coins, he found that they were known as staters and had been minted in Carthage about 350 BC. They were not the earliest of the several currencies that underpinned the Mediterranean economy in the first millennium BC, but they were early enough to be of great archaeological value. Mike did not need to know any of that to guess that these coins would be worth enough to buy Niko a nice new boat with the most modern diving equipment.

There was a long pause while the two men looked at each other. Then Mike said, quietly and thoughtfully: 'An 'undred and eighty feet! It's possible, Niko, possible. You know the problems working down there. The bends and the narcs. But if you do as I tell you . . .'

Then, with Niko staring at him, he began to fantasize a little about the future. You could go deeper with helium. But you had to buy it from America. That took money. But if you did the sums right, sold the products for more than enough to finance the helium supplies . . .

'Look, Niko, let's do it! Let's make this work. Let's make some money and then go deeper. We'll be the first to get down to all those wrecks beyond the reach of your sponge divers. Two hundred and fifty, three 'undred feet, maybe more. There must be so much down there – just waiting.'

Niko smiled broadly. 'Is good! But . . .' The smile vanished dramatically from his face. '. . . Is also bad.'

'Bad?'

'Yes, Mikis. Is against the law. Illegal. The police, they put you in prison.'

'Well, we ain't found nothing yet, 'ave we! Except these two coins. That's not much. Wait a bit: are we breaking the law now, Niko? These coins, what you supposed to do with them?'

'Report. Hand over to government. Then government put in museum.'

'Stuff that! You wanna give these things to a museum?'

Niko shook his head.

'Too bloody right! These are yours, mate! You keep 'em!'

'No, Mikis, my son, that I cannot do.' That lugubrious look again.

'Niko, are you crazy?'

'No, Mikis. We are partners. I cannot keep both. *You* must have one. This I give you. Then we trust each other. And perhaps you need it, yes, to find buyers? Perhaps we then get money?'

'Perhaps. But if you're right, and this wreck is in an 'undred and eighty feet, we don't need much money just yet. All we need is fuel and food. I've got enough for that. When do you want to leave?'

'My friend! My son! I need two days! I must tell my friends they must find another boat. A few I can see here, to others I can send messages. Then I buy fuel and food. Then we go!'

The next morning Sandra came again. This time they had coffee downstairs.

'Gee, I really put the others in hot water . . . Helen lied through her *teeth*, said I'd gone up to the Parthenon, but her parents were still really wild! And I came back and said I was sorry and they made me promise I'd never go out on my own again, what with Daddy coming in a couple of days . . . so I had to tell the other three about you. I swore them to secrecy, and this morning we all went out together, and they're all going to stay out for lunch, and I have to meet them at the Grande Bretagne at three o'clock.'

They went back to his room. There he kissed her, holding her against the door. Her hips pressed against him, searching for his response. Underneath her coat she wore the same skirt, with a silk blouse. He kissed down her neck, pushed back the coat, undid the top button of her blouse and began to pull it out of her skirt.

'We gotta go to bed,' he said. 'You know we gotta go to bed. It's not fair not to. We're both of us going to die otherwise.'

At that moment it felt as if he was telling the truth. She was his whole universe.

And for her, too, delay would have been unthinkable. It was her first time, and the circumstances were so perfect. An attractive, understanding, flattering man, utter privacy, no parental control, and her own desires – how could she possibly say no?

By this time her blouse was undone and his hand was on the bare skin of her back, sliding up underneath the strap of her bra.

'Let me,' she said.

He stood back and unbuttoned his shirt. She carefully took off her coat and hung it on the back of a chair; then her blouse; then her skirt, all of which she hung over the same chair. She stood up, in her bra and panties.

'I had a heap of ironing to do last night,' she said with a quick smile.

Then she came to him and lifted her face up to kiss him. At the same time she reached behind her to undo her bra, and let it fall from her arms.

'Now,' she said, and with a swift movement she stepped out of her panties and got into bed.

He was very careful with her. He said all the right things, and meant them. He told her she was beautiful, that he had never met anyone like her, that he loved her. It was the first time he'd said that to anyone. She was a little apprehensive, then relieved, then passionate. As he had warned her, he finished quickly, and lay for a long time savouring her skin, hair, breasts, lips.

Later they made love again, for longer. There was more talk of love. Later still she rested on him, exploring his face and chest. She was indeed unutterably sweet to touch and see. In that short space of time he had fallen completely in love with her.

'There'll be more in a minute, girl. Much more,' he promised.

He was as good as his word. The third time she was utterly responsivc. It was as if shc'd been at it for years.

They began to talk.

To ensure that she returned the following day, Mike told her about his plans, taking her into his confidence, and impressing her. Then, because she was young, and it was all he had to offer, he told her about Niko and the wreck. He got out of bed, naked, and fetched the gold coin. He showed it to her. She said it was beautiful, then became thoughtful. He told her he'd have to sell it sometime. It was then she said, 'Gee, that's a funny thing.'

His hand was running idly over her stomach and up on to her breast. But her mind was temporarily elsewhere. She bit her bottom lip. 'Daddy has something to do with antiques. He's got a whole heap of stuff. Perhaps he'll buy them off you.'

'Well, that would be nice,' said Mike, and gave no further thought to that part of the conversation.

Shortly afterwards Sandra said she really had to go. It was quarter past two, and they'd been making love, on and off, for two and a half hours.

'Tomorrow?'

'I don't know. I really don't know. It's going to get more and more difficult. I'll try, I really will.'

The next morning she didn't show up. He spent two hours in a state of high sexual tension which was partially resolved at lunchtime when Niko arrived. Tomorrow they would go, early. They had a full day's journey ahead of them and it would be good to travel during daylight hours.

The next morning, after leaving a note for Sandra pinned to his door, Mike boarded the *Hecate*. He had little with him other than the rope-soled sandals and the old navy trousers and shirt he was wearing – just another shirt, some swimming shorts, a toothbrush and a razor. By six o'clock they were off. There was almost nothing moving at that hour except two or three fishing boats looming through the morning mist. Along the marina the launches and yachts of the wealthy rested in silence. Apart from the mewing of the gulls and the thud of their ancient engine, the only sound was the swoosh of a glorious cabin cruiser whose owner was probably going out for some early-morning fishing.

It was a superb, still, spring day, the best time of year to be in Greece. To either side of the silent port the rough-cast hills were dusted with green. The sky was clear but for some high wisps of cloud. Later it would be hot.

They journeyed all day. Once, Niko waved at another vessel. Soon afterwards they drank wine and ate bread. Mike spent most of the day smoking, browning his already tanned body, dozing and steering the course set by Niko.

In the late afternoon, after refuelling the tank just once from the five-gallon cans stored below decks, Niko pointed out an island in the distance. 'Mikonos!' he said.

He halted about a mile away from the island, put the engine at idling speed, then began to zigzag, his eyes darting between Mikonos, two other islands on the horizon and his compass.

'We must line up these three points: the northern tip of Mikonos – the lighthouse there. Can you see it? Then the right-hand point of Tinos at three hundred and fifty-five degrees – almost due north; and that point over there at a hundred and ninety degrees . . . There! Now, Mikis, let me anchor.'

They were too late to dive that evening. Mike swam around the *Hecate* to refresh himself, Niko cooked some spaghetti, they drank wine and then ouzo, and fell asleep.

The next day, after a breakfast of coffee and bread, when the sun was high enough to light the depths, the diving began in earnest.

Mike clambered into his suit while Niko checked their position, before helping him on with the corslet and helmet.

Then there came the heavy boots, the weighted belt, the depth gauge, the knife, torch and a bag, which was to raise small finds, but also contained a crowbar, hacksaw, tape measure and markers.

'OK, Mikis, my son. I look after you. I look after the compressors. I let you out to a hundred and thirty feet. Then I check my position. Then I come back and lower you down to the floor. Then you signal that you are all right. Then I check every damn thing, and you look hard. You give many, many pulls, and I know you find wreck.'

'OK, Niko. But the thing I really care about is coming up. That's a good compressor. But you note the time, make sure your watch is going, look at the bloody tables, OK? See? An hour at that depth and it takes me two hours and twenty-three minutes to come up, stopping at *these* depths for *this* amount of time. Now, I won't stay down much longer than that, because it'll be cold. But if I do, follow the tables, or I'm going to . . .' He crunched his fingers up to imitate the agony of the bends.

'I know, Mikis. Is OK. I understand. You are not Panyotis!'

Niko screwed on the helmet and Mike clambered heavily over the side and down the metal ladder into the water. He took up the slack on his pipe and lifeline, felt Niko's double pat on his helmet, let go of the ladder and hung in the water briefly before dropping into the depths.

As he descended there was no sensation of pressure on his head and lungs, for the compressor on the surface ensured that the air pressure inside his helmet balanced that of the water outside. He did feel the pressure of his suit on his legs, but there was no discomfort.

Landing on sand in the semi-darkness, he waited for Niko to register the absence of weight on the end of the line. Then, as the slack was taken up, he gave the line a single jerk.

He looked around.

The water was clear, but even so his vision was limited to about thirty feet. The seabed was a combination of sand and rocks, and it sloped. His feet sank in hardly at all, kicking up small clouds with each pace. Tiny fish darted out of the darkness and then vanished again.

As his eyes became accustomed to the gloom, he

saw that on one side of him a hill rose another thirty feet; on the other, the sand and rocks ran off downhill into darkness.

He stepped forward to explore, then suddenly stopped in surprise.

In front of him the ground simply vanished. Six feet ahead was the lip of an underwater canyon. At some time in the distant past this must have been the shoreline of an island over which the sea had since risen. He bent to look at the rocks around him. He was standing on a shelf formed by a coral reef, which ran almost due north–south.

There were only two directions to go. He chose north. As a home base he found the *Hecate*'s anchor, walked fifty yards away into the darkness and stuck in one of his markers.

By chance he'd moved off in the right direction. He came upon the wreck a few yards further on. Niko's navigation had been extraordinary – within a hundred yards of the spot.

Directly before him lay the wreck, its shape defined – as Panyotis had reported – by coral and waving lines of seaweed. All the wood exposed to the water had long since vanished, but the basic shape was still there, and had become part of the ocean floor. Contained in the area that had once been the hold lay row upon row of amphorae – the ancient equivalent of plastic bags and tea chests, Mike thought to himself. They were far out of reach of any wave action. Some still stood upright, supported by those on either side. Others, at the edges, had fallen sideways, and scores were broken.

From where he stood, he couldn't see to the edge of the field of pots, for the ship had been large. But it was clear that he was standing near the bows, for the ranks of amphorae narrowed near him and became wider at the limits of his vision.

He walked down the edge of the wreck, counting his paces. It was seventy feet long – a large trading vessel. At the stern the pots had all been broken. Mike guessed there had been a cabin above the hold at this point, which must have collapsed when the ship hit the bottom, or soon after. There were enigmatic rocky bumps scattered among a group of broken pots.

He glanced at his watch. He'd been down twenty minutes.

Remembering the way he had found the coins in Crete, he concentrated on the lumps of rock in the middle of the field of shards. He delivered an experimental kick at one. To his surprise, the little mound burst apart and exploded in a cloud of silt. He squatted down, careful not to let his helmet drop beneath the level of his chest – to avoid a blow-up – and felt beneath the sand.

Under his glove small plates slipped about against each other. He closed his hand and lifted.

Coins. A dozen in one handful. As they rubbed gently against one another in the cupped palms of his hands, he saw that, beneath the light covering of silt and mud, each coin was gold, strangely grey in colour – for at that depth most colour is absorbed by the water above – but gold nevertheless, and as pure as if newly minted.

He opened the bag at his waist and, as carefully as he could, poured them in. A few tumbled slowly to his feet. He retrieved them and began to fumble for more.

Half an hour had gone.

Already he was beginning to feel the cold, for even the Aegean is well below the temperature at which the body operates efficiently. In addition he realized he was beginning to feel just a tiny bit light-headed.

He had just squatted down for the third time when he felt four hard jerks from Niko above: a summons to come up.

But he was not yet ready. What the hell was going on? An hour, he'd said. Niko was worrying too early.

He jerked the lifeline once, indicating that he was still all right. He stooped again, and was holding up a handful of coins, when the lifeline sprang taut so violently that he dropped them.

Jesus! What the bloody hell was the matter with Niko?

He gave the line another, strong tug and bent to retrieve the coins. It took him a few minutes of intense concentration, for they were scattered in little nooks among the pieces of pottery.

He was therefore taken totally by surprise by a violent shove that lifted him off his feet and toppled him over backwards. His arms windmilled slowly as he sought to keep his balance. Automatically he did everything he could to keep his helmet up.

Two thoughts careered through his mind: Fuck, Niko! and then, as he realized he was not being hauled up, Shark! That, too, was unlikely; though there are sharks in the Mediterranean, attacks are almost unknown.

He sat down heavily in a cloud of silt, bringing his nose into sharp contact with the face-plate. As he steadied himself and looked back through the silt, he saw that there was no shark.

But there was another diver.

And he was stooping towards the coins. He seized a handful and began stuffing them into his own bag.

The apparition seemed like a bad dream, some new and evil counterpart to the rapture of the deep. But there was nothing illusory about Mike's tumble, about the blood seeping from his nose and the silt settling around him.

Some other bastard muscling in on his treasure – *his* treasure! The find that was going to guarantee his independence, start a new life for him!

Surprise gave way to violent anger. It never occurred to him not to counter-attack. He rose and stepped forward with no particular plan of action other than to take immediate, unthinking revenge and protect his property.

As he moved, the figure opposite also stood, having finished bagging the handful of coins, looked up, then drew a knife from his belt.

Mike had never got into a fight below water, but he had once spoken to a frogman from Gibraltar who had. The frogman had pointed out that even with a sharp knife it's hard to move fast and strongly enough to penetrate a diving suit. It would take quite a blow to puncture two layers of sheet rubber and a layer of twill. Now, as every film-goer knows, the thing to go for on a frogman is the air tube. The same is true for hard-hat divers, although the pipe is that much tougher.

Mike's attacker was clearly an amateur in such matters. Mike pulled his own knife and made a slow-motion stride almost within striking range. His adversary lunged forward at Mike's midriff, failed to get anywhere near and backed off hastily to one side, towards the edge of the abyss.

Mike had been down forty minutes. He was cold, slow and vulnerable. He was breathing heavily. Despite all this, or perhaps because of it, he suddenly felt supremely self-confident. But he was experienced enough to realize that he was suffering from the first effects of the narcs. He was in no state to fight. There had to be another way, for he was not at all certain how much longer he could hang on to his declining faculties. He had to think fast. His adversary was coming at him again. The chances were he was going to get through sometime and if Mike was only semi-conscious, even his suiting and a tough pipe wouldn't save him.

Suddenly Mike saw what he had to do. He was held to the seabed by the weight of his suit, which was partially buoyed up by the air inside his helmet. It was possible to make himself lighter by adjusting the air intake. It was a trick that took some skill, for too much air would lead to a blow-up, and he needed more than partial buoyancy to achieve what he had in mind.

He reached into his bag, felt around for his hacksaw and withdrew it. Then, as he adjusted his intake valve, he felt the rush of air into his helmet, the slight surge down over his chest and the sudden lightness. Praying he'd got the balance right, he pushed himself forwards and upwards, jumping as hard as he could. Still in slow motion, he took off towards his attacker's helmet. He saw the knife slicing towards him and felt a blow on his leg. But by that time he was kicking at the helmet itself, to give himself another boost upwards. He was suddenly out of reach of the flailing arm below, and gripping tight to his enemy's air pipe. Now it seemed he had all the time in the world.

Holding the pipe in one hand and his hacksaw in the other, he sawed at the tough rubber. As soon as the teeth bit, the pipe divided neatly, blasting bubbles out into the water around him. The lifeline parted even more easily: he cut through it in seconds.

Eight feel below him, the helmeted figure was lunging hopelessly upwards when the cut hose snaked down gently across his helmet.

The stricken diver dropped his knife and twiddled his air valve. Then he seized the hose and held it up in front of him in a gesture of incomprehension. Mike, meanwhile, was still suspended above him, hanging on to the cut line. He was still a few pounds heavier than water, and had no intention of drifting down into the reach of the desperate man below.

His victim was already as good as dead. He wouldn't drown, for at the end of each pipe is a one-way valve that blocks water. Nor would he die of the squeeze, because the remaining few breaths of air in the helmet were at the same pressure as the water outside.

No: he would die of asphyxiation, and the process would take several minutes.

Mike hung above, watching with a combination of relief and horror the death throes of the figure below.

The man held his air pipe pleadingly towards Mike. He went down on his knees and struck the sand with one arm, as if protesting at the unfairness of it all. Then he stood up and tottered backwards, stepping towards the edge of the cliff. Mike had a glimpse through the face-plate of the wide-open, silently screaming mouth, saw the terror-stricken eyes. After that the diver took another pace back, felt the ocean floor falling away beneath his boot, waved his arms in a dying attempt to keep balance, then slowly tumbled over backwards. In a final spasm a leg kicked and he began a slow somersault into the darkness. Before he vanished, Mike saw the legs go rigid as the gas in the suit escaped from the helmet. Now the head would be in a partial vacuum and its owner mercifully unconscious. The last view Mike had was of the dim figure sinking upside down into the depths. He knew even then that in later years he would dream of that sight and perhaps imagine himself dying in such a way. Not a blow-up exactly; more a blow-down – a unique death in diving history.

Only then did he let go his line, drift slowly back to the floor, readjust his air intake and give the double tug which signified he was to be brought up.

On the way he realized dreamily – for he was barely conscious himself – that whoever was tending the dead man must soon notice that something was amiss. There would be no immediate difference in the weight, for he had not been suspended; and it took as much pressure to blow air down the cut pipe as if there was a diver on the end; but there would be *something* – his own gymnastic addition to the line, perhaps, or the sudden blank in the phone link.

According to plan, he rose slowly to seventy feet, then hung for five minutes while the nitrogen that had gathered in his tissues began to seep out of his muscles and blood. Decompressing after an hour at a hundred and eighty feet would be a tedious business. From seventy feet there would be a pause every ten feet, each pause longer than the last. At ten feet he would have to hang in the water for all of thirty-five minutes. He moved up to sixty feet, and began to feel a little better physically.

Mentally, though, he was still in poor shape, in an agony of shock and frustration. This was the first time he had ever killed a man hand to hand, and he had done it so easily, driven by anger and his desire for revenge. He had no idea who the diver was, nor how he came to be there. Niko must have some answers. Christ! If only he had bothered to buy some decent gear with a phone link before setting off on this insane expedition!

At that moment he heard through his helmet the distant thud of motors. He glanced up. The shadow that was the *Hecate* had begun to move. An instant later his line snapped upwards. As the boat accelerated, so the sideways pressure of water began to swing him towards the surface. He was rising quickly, far too quickly. Not only that: the moving shadow above him was getting closer. Niko was winding in the line as fast as the capstan would turn.

'You silly cunt!' Mike shouted uselessly in his helmet. 'You'll fuckin' cripple me!'

When he hit the surface less than half a minute later, his world became a mass of surging spray and his limbs were pinned back by the current. Fortunately, the *Hecate*'s top speed was no more than ten knots. Mike began to swing and bang helplessly against her side, and then, in one of his wild gyrations, he noticed that the diving ladder was right beside him. He steadied himself against it and with the remnants of his strength hauled himself on to it. It took him an age to climb each step, but he finally struggled clear of the rushing water and stuck his helmet over the edge of the gunwale.

Niko saw him, shouted and made waving signs to show he was on his way. He cast an anxious glance behind him and abandoned the wheel to help Mike aboard. That part was a nightmare: even for two people, 350lb of human flesh and diving equipment is tough to ship. When the diver inside is close to collapse, it is nearly impossible.

Mike lay on his back like a dying beetle while Niko scrabbled with his face-plate, and then, even before Mike could scream out the question that was surging within him, Niko pointed over Mike's shoulder.

Mike sat up and looked aft.

Some two hundred yards away a cabin cruiser was creaming along in their wake.

'He chase us!' shouted Niko, helping Mike off with his helmet. 'They come after us! They put down diver!'

He returned hastily to the wheel, leaving Mike to struggle with the rest of his gear. 'I try to warn you. But they pull up empty hose. No diver! I think something happen down there. Maybe, Mikis, he do this thing. They shout! I go! They come! Now we have trouble.'

Mike had dropped his weights and was sitting in his clammy suit, gripping the gunwale, exhausted, staring back at the launch.

'Yeah,' he shouted back at Niko. 'Big trouble. Like not long from now I'm going to be bent like an old tin can.' He began to struggle out of his suit. 'That bugger down there tried to kill me. So I cut 'is pipe for 'im.'

'Ah, Mikis, now they going to get us!'

The cruiser was almost upon them. She was at least twice as long as the *Hecate*, at least twice as fast and possibly four times as heavy.

'Blimey,' said Mike, 'them blokes can really move.'

He stepped out of his suit, so that he was wearing only his swimming trunks and a T-shirt.

It was clear they were trapped.

A voice boomed out over a loudspeaker: 'Pull over or we ram you!'

'We can't do a bloody thing, Niko,' said Mike, who was too tired and apprehensive about his own condition to care any more. 'Pull over. I've got to get back below.'

'They kill us!' Niko said, his face set.

The white cruiser was twenty yards away – he

could now see her name, *Argo*, quite clearly – and closing.

Suddenly Niko threw the wheel of the *Hecate* over. Mike was not at all clear what he was up to – perhaps trying to swing her round so fast that he could head away in the opposite direction before the large cruiser had time to turn. But the *Argo*'s own performance was that of a greyhound compared with a snail. As the *Hecate* turned, the *Argo*'s stern dug in, her bows swung round and within ten seconds she was upon the *Hecate* amidships. Mike, who was gripping the gunwale again, was catapulted over the side and, as the waters closed over him, had time to think of only one thing: go deep, avoid the props.

He could swim no more than a few yards underwater. He had no idea in what direction he had gone, but realized as he surfaced that the roar of engines had ceased.

He'd come up about ten yards to the rear of the cruiser, a little to one side. He could see members of the crew up in the bows peering down over the side. Of the *Hecate* there was no sign. Wreckage littered the surface of the sea. There were no other ships close by, and no islands close to hand. He trod water. No one saw him.

There was no hope of escape. Indeed, the very attempt would have meant death or, at least, supreme agony. He was cold and exhausted, and his consciousness was clouded again. He knew that in his veins there would already be forming the little bubbles of nitrogen gas that over the next few hours would create a hell equivalent to withdrawal from heroin. He had nothing to lose by going on board, and perhaps a lot to gain, for the cruiser offered the only conceivable way of avoiding the bends.

'Here!' he shouted, and waved.

There was an answering shout, and a young man on the *Argo*'s bow pointed to him. He began to swim a slow side-stroke towards the cruiser.

By the time he reached it a ladder was in position. He paused for a while on the part of the ladder that was underwater. It was a long way up, and he could hardly move.

At the top of the steps his arms were seized. The treatment was rough, but he hardly noticed. He was too exhausted to do anything for himself any more. Young men's voices, talking in Greek, told him to come on. He found it much easier to close his eyes and let them drag him.

In the well of the boat they sat him dripping on the deck. He collapsed sideways. He opened his eyes once, and saw that one of the men had gone.

He breathed deeply, still conscious. No pain yet.

The other young man returned. He was lifted again. They balanced him on his feet as if they were testing some sort of toy.

'You can stand? You can hear?'

'Reckon so,' he said.

'We go now down steps. You look out. No fall.'

They led him below decks, through a pair of double doors and down a companion-way. His head lolled. He saw nothing but his own feet. The men put him on a chair. He leant forward and put his head in his hands.

A voice probed his fogged consciousness.

'Well, Mr Michael Cox, you have some talking to do.' The voice was deep, American, and with a hint of something that was not American.

Mike looked up.

In front of him, leaning back into a leather sofa, was the grossest figure he had ever seen. The man was wearing a white jellaba which swept over the bulk of flesh, unifying the separate masses of chest, paunch and thighs. Yet the man did not look unhealthy. From the solidity of his neck and shoulders, Mike could see that his was the bulk not just of obesity, but also of muscle. There was a black moustache. The head was bald. The eyes were dark, intense and powerful, and at that moment fixed unwaveringly on Mike.

''Oo the 'ell are you?' Mike said.

'You do not know me.' It was a statement not a question. 'That's fine, just fine. But I know you, Mr Cox, and I need to, because you've just killed a man who was part of this ship's crew. I want to know what happened, and you're going to tell me.

You will give me no trouble, because trouble means time wasted, and we both know what that means for you. You know and I know that you should still be hanging over the side decompressing. Not very long from now, Mr Cox, you're going to have a problem. So let me hear from you.'

The big man lay back, spread his huge arms along the back of the sofa and smiled in anticipation. But Mike, tired and frightened as he was, did not feel ready to talk.

If he explained why he was down there, he would reveal the treasure, and lose it. But wait . . . How come the cabin cruiser had turned up precisely at that moment? And what was there about it that was vaguely familiar? He couldn't think. He had to play for time.

'What you done with Niko?'

'Niko? Ah, the idiot who tried to run away with you.' The great shoulders heaved themselves into a shrug. 'A crazy man. He put himself right under our bows. We looked for him, but . . .'

Mike felt a twinge in his right elbow. It was starting. He winced.

'Yes. I shouldn't like you to suffer *too* much, Mr Cox. I want to know your story, and I want to know it fast. I have two other suits aboard and good equipment. We can decompress you easily enough simply by dropping you back over the side. But not before I have your story.'

Mike's left knee screamed at him. Was it really

worth risking paralysis for the sake of a few coins?

No, it wasn't.

He began to talk. He supposed he should be talking about the coins. The big man interrupted once or twice to ask about Mike's own background. When Mike told him about the attack on the seabed, his interrogator breathed: 'Fool! Idiot!' Otherwise he made no comment.

At the end of another fifteen minutes Mike was feeling random, shooting pains in several parts of his body and was moving and bending almost constantly in an attempt to relieve the symptoms. When he had finished, the big man said: 'So it was all true.'

''Oo the 'ell *are* you? And 'ow did you . . . ?' Mike broke off, grimacing and straightening his right leg. He bent it again, then stood and almost immediately doubled over to relieve the pain in his back.

'I think we'll leave all that until later. First, I need your agreement on a plan I wish to see completed. We shall return to the site of your wreck, and you will lift the coins for me. Then we shall see . . . Don't even think of arguing, Mr Cox. It will waste your valuable time.'

Mike's elbows felt as if they were being held in a vice. He stared out from his agony at the fat man. 'Yes,' was all he said.

The fat man grinned again.

'You're a wise man, Mr Cox. Now, we shall save your life.'

On deck everything was ready. The orders must have been given before Mike was ever brought below. He was hurried into a hard-hat suit that had scarcely been used. A compressor started. He was helped over the side.

Within two minutes he was hanging seventy feet down, in the womb of the ocean, and the agonizing, hard pains began to recede as the pressure of the water around him and of the air inside his suit pushed the nitrogen bubbles back into solution in his blood and flesh.

He heard a voice: this suit had a telephone. Above, there was someone who knew what he was doing. Between the two of them they established a margin of safety.

It would take Mike over two hours to come back to the surface, resting every ten feet for progressively long intervals – ten minutes at sixty feet, fifteen at fifty feet – until the final thirty-five minutes at ten feet. For the time being, he was safe.

He wondered again who his captor was, how he came to be there, how he knew Mike's name. Questions, questions, and no answers. But at least the pain had gone. He was too exhausted to concentrate any more. During the last two stoppages he dozed.

* * *

By mid-morning he was back in the same cabin, with two sandwiches and a glass of milk in front of him. He had been given a clean shirt and some shorts.

'Tired, Mr Cox?' said the big man, who had apparently not moved from his position on the leather sofa since Mike's first arrival on board. 'But strong, huh? That's good. Because you're going down again in an hour.'

Mike was drained of energy and emotion. Dead-eyed, he met the man's gaze.

'That's ridiculous,' he said. 'You want my coins, the least you could do is allow me time to recover.'

'Time we do not have. And you know as well as I that your slight attack of the bends did no lasting damage.' He sighed, as if confronting a difficult child. 'You really have no choice. I can put you back down there by force, if I so decide. Must we start the same game all over again?'

'Fuck you, mate. When do I find out what's going on?'

'Afterwards, Mr Cox, afterwards.'

So Mike was taken to a cabin, allowed to rest and fed again – all under the gaze of one of the young Greek crewmen. For half an hour he heard nothing but the muffled, throaty throb of the engine and the rush of the bow-wave; felt nothing but the rise and fall of the boat; saw nothing but his room, for the porthole was curtained.

As he lay, eyes closed, thoughts raced through

his mind. His many questions would have to wait for answers. His most immediate concern was to ensure that his captor did not get all the treasure. He would have to bring up some coins, of course, but surely not all of them.

It was an obvious enough idea, and was of course pre-empted by the big man himself. As Mike was being helped back into his suit, he said: 'I want *all* those coins, Mr Cox. I want a running commentary on what you see and do. And two other things: firstly, I will allow you one in ten of the coins you retrieve. The more you bring, the more we both get. Secondly, after you come up, I shall make sure that no one will ever come back. As we leave, later this afternoon, we shall destroy the site. It would pain me to think of you, or anyone else, returning at some later date.'

This time it was easy. The equipment was good, the tender experienced, the positioning spot on, the coins themselves easy to find. There were perhaps two hundred in all, each one solid gold. The vessel had probably been carrying the cash back home after a successful voyage. The amphorae had probably contained wine and oil for sale at home, wherever that was. In addition to the coins he found a dozen little ivory statues and two amphorae, almost intact, with traces of painting on them. He described his work over the phone link, as instructed, and sent up his finds in a cage dropped down to him. He saw no way of keeping anything for himself. He was trapped.

By the evening he was up on deck again. The big man was as good as his word. Two crewmen stood at the stern and dropped a couple of charges. As the cruiser pulled clear, the surface of the sea erupted into two gouts of spray.

Then there was an evening meal in the same darkened cabin. The big man joined him. He had changed into a white cotton suit, well tailored to his bulk.

'You're in trouble, big trouble, Mr Cox,' he said. 'I'll spell it out for you. For starters, you've been exploring a wreck, with antiquities aboard, and clearly had no intention of reporting the find to the authorities. That could land you a hefty jail sentence.

'But the real problem is that you've killed a man, Mr Cox. Not just any man, either. His name was David Kellogg, and he was the son of a very rich and very influential family in Boston. That could prove really very nasty. For murdering a foreign national you could be locked up here in Greece for a long time, pending extradition proceedings. If you were lucky you'd be tried back in the old US of A. It would take a while, and none of it would be pleasant.

'The third reason why you're in trouble, Mr Cox, is that my name is Milovan Krassnik.'

'Krassnik!'

The big man saw Mike's expression.

'Yes, sir*ee*!' he said, in an overdone Deep South accent, smiling benignly. 'You been layin' ma little girl, Michael. May I call you Michael? And I'd say she was a mite young for that. What do *you* say?' The smile disappeared from his face, leaving an expression of implacable malevolence.

A number of things fell into place. Obvious, really. Sandra had seen the coin. She knew about the treasure. She knew Mike's plans. And – with his permission, for God's sake – had spilled the whole thing to her old man. The yacht that had been pulling out of the harbour as they left . . . Yes, now he remembered. Krassnik must have been shadowing them all the previous day, had them in telescopic view that morning, saw that Mike had gone down, guessed the wreck had been found, then tried to beat him to the draw.

'You want my advice?' Krassnik went on. 'Don't say a damn thing. You're all wrapped up, and you know it.' He grinned again, and bent forward, menacingly. 'So listen, and listen well. I could kill you now. But that would not be in my interests. I have in mind a rather more productive relationship for us both. I have good connections. So, apparently, do you, and you are a very experienced diver. Here is the deal: you find statues, coins – anything I can sell. In return, I'll look after you. Income, equipment, protection, especially protection. Think about it, Michael – but you will find you have no choice.

You are, to the Greek government, a thief and a murderer. I have friends in many places. Much better to work for me and be rich, than risk the inside of a Greek jail . . . or worse.'

''Ow long do you think this . . . relationship will last?'

Krassnik shrugged. 'Who knows? Until we stop making money.'

'And Sandra?'

'Alexandra will forget you. My plans for her do not include a penniless adventurer from the slums of London. She needs wealth and power, you see. She will have them, and when she is ready . . . I see you are not disposed to argue. Very wise.'

He leant across to a desk on his right, pressed a button on an intercom and said: 'Ask Miss Sandra to come in, please.'

It was the first indication Mike had had that Sandra was on board. She must have been kept as firmly under control as he himself had been.

She had been crying a lot. Barefoot, wearing shorts and a white blouse, she would have looked quite delectable if she hadn't also looked utterly broken. There was an ugly red mark on one cheek. Krassnik patted the sofa beside him, and Sandra sat, downcast. Then her head came up, and she looked at Mike.

'It's all my fault. I'm sorry,' she said.

Krassnik patted her knee.

'My dear, that is not the first time you have seen

me respond purely as a businessman. Do not pretend to be shocked. I needed information. You had no choice. You were not to know what I wanted to do. Do not blame yourself for what happened to your friend here.'

'You're a right bastard, Krassnik. What sort of father 'its 'is own daughter?'

'I do, when she needs to be reminded of whose daughter she is and of her responsibilities. I have a position, have I not? Hmm?'

'Yes, Daddy.'

'Right. And I don't send you to good schools and have you meet the best people to have you playing around with asshole divers as soon as my back is turned.'

He spoke quietly, but there was no doubt about his anger or the terror he inspired in Sandra. Mike felt the hair on the back of his head prickle. He had never been in the presence of someone so clearly used to exercising naked power. Beneath the veneer of smiles and politeness, Krassnik was a terror.

He was like that for a number of quite simple reasons. He had been poor, an outsider, a member of a divided and weak nation. He grew up aching to be rich, to belong and to wield power. Wealth he had acquired. Status he was in the process of acquiring: it went with wealth; and he had married well, but Sandra was to complete the process for him. Power . . . well, power he preferred to exercise behind the scenes, internationally, in a way Mike was not to discover for several years.

He had other interests, of course, of which supplying works of art was one. They were useful keys to various social and political doors; hence his professional interest in Mike.

'If I hadn't told him about your coin . . .' Sandra said pitifully to Mike.

'Come on, girl,' Mike replied. 'It was my fault for telling you about the thing in the first place.'

She shot him a smile through her tears.

Krassnik spread his hands and smiled as if to say, 'Well, now! What was all the fuss about?' but added: 'You should both sleep now. For obvious reasons you will be in your own cabins. Do not try to leave, please. The doors will be locked, and my men have good ears.'

They docked in Piraeus at dusk the next evening, with Mike and Sandra still in their cabins.

The following morning a small delegation came aboard – a police officer and an American Embassy official with his secretary. Krassnik told Mike later that he had dictated statements concerning the unfortunate business with Niko and the young American, David Kellogg. Niko's family would be adequately compensated, better than they would have been if he had died from diving too deep and too long; and the American family would be informed of their grievous loss. There would be questions, of course. But the answers would be convincing. David was an inexperienced diver . . . he insisted on going down . . . a deep wreck . . . his discovery of coins . . . his refusal to respond to signals . . . the attempt to raise him by force . . . the sharp coral . . . the cut pipe . . . the disappearance . . . appalling tragedy. Krassnik himself would go to Boston, offer condolences and be present at the memorial service.

Mike stayed on in Piraeus, in the same room, this time with funds. He elected to sell his share of the coins – twenty of them – to Krassnik, who offered him $2000 in cash.

His freedom was a mere technicality. Krassnik owned him. There was no way out. Flight would have meant his name being given to the Greek police, to the British police and eventually, he assumed, to Interpol. Life would not be worth living. Besides, there was Sandra. Her sudden removal enshrined her in his mind as an ideal. In erotic dreams, in the arms of other women whose names he could hardly remember, he summoned up the image of Sandra and that one supreme afternoon of lovemaking. He wanted her as he was never to want any woman again: and the only way back to her was through Krassnik.

It seemed to Mike that the way to win a modicum of independence was to become a more equal partner in their one-sided relationship. To do that he would have to know more about Krassnik, would have to have some sort of hold over him and beat him at his own game.

It would not be quick, for Krassnik could vanish into his own particular jungle without leaving any clue by which an inquisitive outsider might track him.

9

For five years Mike waited, and both men profited. Mike found another partner and another sponge-diving boat. He equipped it with the best Siebe–Gorman diving gear and compressors. He even did a good deal of sponge diving with his little team.

His real work, however, was to identify and clear ancient wrecks. Business was not startling. Few treasure hunters get rich. Mike made a living only because he was careful. He worked deep and was fanatical about safety. Most of his finds were amphorae, which fetched a standard price on Krassnik's market and were transferred to his yacht once every month during the summer.

Only once did Mike make a major find. He raised a collection of a dozen figurines, each only a few inches high, whose heads were smooth, without eyes or mouths, but with noses. The arms were held in a curious way against their chest. Krassnik became extremely interested when he saw them, and Mike ended up $10,000 richer.

In the winter Mike spent time in England researching new equipment. In 1953 he acquired one of the first commercial scuba apparatuses from the newly formed British Sub-Aqua Club.

During all this time he had no idea how Krassnik made his real money. Clearly antiquities were just a sideline, a way of keeping friends happy and buying himself status. There was no clue to his activities aboard the *Argo* that Mike ever saw when he went aboard. Occasionally she would lie up for weeks, tended only by her crew, with no sign of Krassnik, who worked from a hotel suite and spent a good deal of time elsewhere.

Mike's situation was intensely galling. He dared not return to England to plan the realization of his own long-standing ambition. He was all too aware that a premature move would invite Krassnik's revenge and ensure that there would never be any chance of a return to the *Edinburgh*. Besides, he was not yet ready to abandon his dream of Sandra. She was in fact now married with a child and another on the way, living in a charming brownstone in the best part of Boston, but Krassnik had no intention of destroying Mike's idealized longings with cold reality.

Mike's frustration was made worse by the knowledge that Krassnik himself would be extremely interested in the *Edinburgh*. He might even back him. But the idea of approaching his gross, devious and vicious employer as a potential partner struck

Mike as plain stupid. He couldn't trust him. He would merely be sticking his head further into the noose. No: he had to escape from Krassnik. And that demanded information.

In late 1954 Mike made his move. He bought a small radio transmitter. He experimented with it by listening in on the café downstairs. By later standards there was nothing small about it, but it was neat enough to smuggle aboard the *Argo* on one of his monthly summer visits to hand over his undersea findings.

He was shown as usual into Krassnik's cabin, and was left alone pending his arrival. He took the opportunity to remove the radio from the bag containing his findings, and place it in an air vent above the porthole.

That evening, in his room a mile away from the *Argo*'s mooring, he tuned in. The device worked well enough, and for several evenings he listened to talk, in both English and Greek, about politics, social life, finance. The information was mostly meaningless or useless, since it was extremely disjointed as a result of the speakers moving round the cabin or continuing the conversation elsewhere.

Then, suddenly, jackpot.

On this particular evening, at about half past nine, Krassnik had received two, perhaps three, men on board. As they came into the *Argo*'s main cabin, the conversation began inconsequentially with an offer of coffee and mutters of assent.

'A moment . . .' There was the sound of a door opening and shutting, then: 'Very well, we are agreed.' Krassnik must have now been sitting at his desk, directly beneath the transmitter, for his voice reached Mike clearly. He was referring to some previous discussion: 'Colonel Nasser wished me to make preliminary contacts. These should lead to your country's acquisition of a substantial supply of new weaponry in the near future. You will tell the colonel that I shall specifically not speak to my American or British sources.'

More murmurs of assent.

'May I ask, gentlemen, what assurance I have that your colonel is to be trusted? I am aware, of course, that Mr Naguib has resigned as prime minister; but Mr Naguib is still president. Am I to understand that the deputy prime minister is solely responsible for your country's new policy as regards arms purchases?'

There were some words, of which Mike could catch only: 'Muslim brotherhood . . . enemies of Egypt . . . little information . . . immediate action.'

'Very well. Since I need not at this stage place firm orders, I believe I can take the risk. I happen to know . . .' At this point Krassnik himself must have turned or moved, for his voice died to a murmur before resuming: '. . . on offer by Czechoslovakia. It is widely known that such arms are of Russian . . . see what can be done . . .'

The talk became broken as Krassnik moved about,

then more general, concerning travel arrangements and dates and venues of future meetings. By now Mike's attention had wandered.

So: it was arms dealing. That made sense, for it was well known that Israel and the Arabs were arming themselves as fast as they could, from every available source. Even before the 1948 war Israel had acquired a motley collection of weapons from America's Second World War scrap heaps. She had also acquired Mauser rifles, Avia fighters and modified Messerschmitts from Czechoslovakia. Thereafter, she had bought small arms from Belgium, machine-guns from Spain, American tanks. In 1953 France's Dassault company offered Ouragan and Mystère fighters to Israel, a deal that was partly financed by the USA. Meanwhile both Britain and America supported the Arabs with arms, thus attempting to preserve a rough balance in the Middle East.

Nasser's rise to power changed this. In 1954 he was yet to emerge as Egypt's strong man. Suez was still two years away. But he was already in a position of considerable – if unconsolidated – influence, and determined to avoid automatic alignment with the West. During 1954 he began to seek arms from elsewhere. Hence his interest in Soviet arms, and hence Krassnik's involvement at this delicate stage in the negotiations.

Mike knew none of the details and was no political expert, but it was clear to him that Krassnik, as an American, was skating on thin ice. To act as an agent for Russian arms was surely treasonable. Was that bloke McCarthy still accusing everyone of being Commies? And wasn't an accusation like that enough to ruin a career? What would be the result if the American police, the FBI or the State Department, or whatever, knew one of their nationals was buying arms from the Russkies and selling them to Egypt, just when Egypt was kicking the Yanks in the teeth?

Two days later Mike returned to his room after doing some maintenance work on his boat. Two men were waiting in the corridor leading to the stairway. They were Krassnik's crewmen, two of those who had manhandled Mike on his first acquaintance with the American. They were not men to argue with.

'He wants to see you,' one of them said curtly.

Mike knew what he meant, but tried to stall. 'OK. Tomorrow morning?'

'Now.'

They escorted him in silence along the quayside to the *Argo*.

On board, Krassnik waved him into the armchair, while the two men stood back.

On Krassnik's desk lay Mike's little transmitter.

'Yes?' said Mike, all innocence. 'What's up?'

Krassnik sighed, as if dealing with a recalcitrant teenager. 'This was found. It has a range of no more than a mile. I cannot believe that there is anyone else that close who would want to place such a device aboard the *Argo*, or be in a position to do so. Clearly you are an amateur in such things. Such a goddamn stupid thing to do, and a stupid place to put it. And Georgios here naturally found the receiver in your room. I was foolish to be so lenient with you. First, of course, I need to know who is paying you and to whom you have imparted your information.'

'I don't know what . . .'

'Come, Michael, we have little time,' said Krassnik, speaking more quietly. 'If my safety is at stake I may have to move fast. If that happens your life is not worth *that*.' He snapped his finger and thumb casually.

'There's no one.'

'Please, don't be foolish. Better talk now while you still can.'

'Look, Krassnik, there really isn't anyone. I was just bloody fed up not knowing what you did for a living. I was curious.'

'Yes. And Georgios and his friend are curious to know how you respond to a little persuasion. You already know the game, of course. You remember the rules – into the suit, over the side. But the rules have changed. No compressors this time. You will feel pressure, even at ten feet. At twenty feet, with no extra air in your helmet, you will start bleeding from the nose, ears, mouth and eyes. At fifty feet, if you're still conscious, you will have the interesting experience of feeling your stomach being forced up your windpipe. Naturally, at any time you'll be able to call a halt by telling me what I want to know. You like the sound of the game?'

'For Christ's sake! I don't know any fuckin' thing! At least I only know what I 'eard, which is that you're involved with some deal in Egypt, but I don't know anybody that . . .'

'I see you do not yet take me seriously. We shall proceed at once.'

Krassnik pressed the intercom button, and while Mike sat frozen in impotent fear and rage, the *Argo*'s engine hauled her aft, out of her berth, and then, with a surge of power, drove her towards the open sea.

A few miles out, Georgios and his young associate forced Mike up to the deck. There lay the suit.

'I suggest you do not struggle,' Krassnik said. 'If you do they'll have to knock you out. And then you might not be able to talk in time.'

Mike was already in the suit when his racing mind made a connection.

'Listen, Krassnik. I can't tell you anything because I don't 'ave any bloody contacts. Believe me. Just one thing. You want to make money from me. Well, I can suggest a way of making so much money you'd never need to worry about bloody weapons again.'

This time Krassnik took notice. 'Talk,' he said.

So, standing there in the diving suit, the corslet and helmet lying beside him, the boat silent in mid-ocean, Mike told Krassnik about the *Edinburgh* and the gold.

'I was there. You ask Sandra. I told her.' Krassnik's

eyes narrowed fractionally at the mention of his daughter's name. 'I know where it is in the ship. I know 'ow much – over five tons of it. Five bloody tons of pure Russian gold!'

'What are you suggesting?'

'That I get it for you, of course. I'm no use to you in this business any more.'

Mike was beginning to make sense. The returns were scarcely worth the investment in time and money. Eventually, Krassnik knew, the police would pick Mike up, protection or no. Then the game would be over for the diver. But if he could be useful in another game . . . Five tons of gold! That was something worth playing for. It wasn't even much of a risk, for both men would be forced to trust each other by the nature of the information each possessed.

'Come on, Krassnik.' Mike drew strength from the respite. 'At least ask me some more questions.'

Krassnik gestured to his two goons. 'You're a lucky man, Michael,' he said, turning away to the stairs leading down to his cabin. 'A very lucky man.'

His suggestion undoubtedly saved Mike's life, even if it gave him less than the freedom he longed for. Indeed, it was to bind him to Krassnik, though at a greater geographical remove, for many years to come.

Back in Piraeus there were more questions.

Krassnik did some checking of his own, while detaining Mike on board. After two days he returned and told him: 'I believe you about the gold. I believe it will one day be lifted. But it is not possible now. So when? And what guarantee is there we can do it first?'

Mike began to talk, of his ambition and of the technical problems. We know air is no good at much over three hundred feet, he explained, because the nitrogen gave you all sorts of problems. But there was a gas that got over a lot of these problems – helium. This had to come from the States, and it was very expensive. And there were other problems with helium as well. It affected your vocal cords and made you sound all squeaky, which was dangerous if you were trying to get across information. And it was also a very good conductor of heat. So, if the water outside was cold, you died like you were in a deep freeze.

'But it's a fast-developing field,' he added. 'The ideas are all there. A lot of work's going on in scuba gear, rigid suits, submersibles, different sorts of gas combinations – also to get deeper and overcome the bends and the narcs. We may 'ave to wait a few years, but Christ, what's a few years when you're talking about making millions?'

Krassnik heard him out because he had already made up his mind. He really had nothing to lose by going along with the scheme. Murder was easy, but messy. And he had no wish any longer to risk

Mike's continued presence in the area, especially when his own business was expanding so fast and unpredictably. His only problem was how to keep tabs on him, and ensure that when the time came they would be in business together.

'OK, Michael, you have a deal. But I don't want any trouble from you. So I have one final element to add to the equation. Take this, and this.' He pushed a piece of paper and a ball-point pen across the table.

'You're going to write what I tell you to write, and then you're going to sign it. OK? Now write: 'I, the undersigned, Michael Cox, wish to declare that I am solely responsible for the death of David Kellogg. I killed him on April 20, 1950, in the following circumstances . . .'

Krassnik saw that Mike was not writing. He looked resigned as he pointed to the piece of paper.

'What do you think I am, Krassnik? Ready to sign my own fuckin' death warrant?'

'That's no death warrant, Michael. It's merely an investment on my part to make sure that you treat me right. I want you to be in no doubt that if you should ever double-cross me, if you should ever try to do this deal without me, your life won't be worth living. If I don't get you, the police will. You'll be a fugitive for life. Besides' – he smiled disarmingly – 'I'm not even asking you to tell a lie. We'll get the circumstances down just as you told me.'

'Jesus Christ! The bloke attacked me! I 'ad no choice!'

'That's OK, Mike. We'll say that if it makes you happy. But it won't stop the police wanting to interview you. And it sure as hell won't stop the family making a God-awful fuss. Now, shall we proceed? Don't give me a reason for putting you back in that diving suit.'

10

In a sense Mike did win his freedom from Krassnik. He was free of him for far longer than he would have imagined possible. For twenty-two years he was free.

Sometimes, after a gap of a year or more, he would realize that there had been no contact during that time. Sometimes he allowed himself the hope that Krassnik had forgotten. But then, eventually, there would be a letter or a call from some minion who had no idea who Mike was. 'A message from Mr Krassnik,' the voice would say. 'He wants to hear from you.' That was all.

It was all that was necessary. Then Mike would set aside an hour or two one evening and write to the address he'd been given, a box number in Washington, New York or Paris, with details of his own situation and a review of technical developments in diving and his latest prognosis for the raising of the gold.

His own words, spoken in desperation that afternoon aboard the *Argo*, turned out to be wildly optimistic. True, it was in theory possible to dive deep enough to reach the *Edinburgh*. A deep-water submersible could have got down there, a machine like the *Trieste*, perhaps, which in 1960 plunged nearly seven miles to the bottom of the Mariana Trench, the deepest place known on earth.

Or a diving-bell. Divers in bells went ever deeper by replacing nitrogen with helium, and experimenting with arcane combinations of gases, the proportions of which varied with depth. In 1961 a Swiss diver, Hannes Keller, and the editor of *Life*, Kenneth MacLeish, went down to seven hundred and twenty-five feet in Lake Maggiore, Italy.

Or an armoured diving-suit, which protected the diver from the effects of pressure in great Michelin-man swirls of metal.

Depth was not the problem. But none of these devices would, in Mike's opinion, ever be flexible or manoeuvrable enough to salvage a ship in several hundred feet of icy water. The problem was to get divers in flexible suits down deep enough and long enough to do the work, and still allow them to breathe, communicate and keep warm.

A rapid dive overcame the need for extended decompression, but left no time for useful work. To spend more than a few minutes at five hundred feet meant many hours of decompression – a hopelessly uneconomic activity. Unless the diver was inside a decompression chamber by then, he might die of cold. Even working at shallow depths with helium involved the peculiar problem of communication: in helium the vocal cords vibrate more rapidly, so that even a basso profondo sounds like Mickey Mouse. For all these reasons it was simply not worthwhile to work hard-hat or scuba divers at depths much below three hundred feet.

Mike wrote to Krassnik year after year to reiterate these problems. He was in a good position to know what he was talking about, for he had returned to a well-paid job with a Southampton salvage firm. The work kept him in touch. But the techniques would have been familiar enough to a diver of the 1930s. There were refinements, but as yet no fundamental changes.

For sixteen years Mike lived in Southampton, a bachelor, lusty enough for several years, but increasingly isolated by his two obsessions: the lesser one with Sandra, whose image faded with the years but who had effectively spoiled him for any relationship that might have led to marriage; the other, with the *Edinburgh* and her gold. During all this time the most he could do towards salvaging the gold was to research the circumstances of her sinking from a diver's point of view, and the problems of returning to her.

After some reading in the Public Records Office, and some discreet enquiries at the Ministry of Defence, these became depressingly clear. For a start, no one knew exactly where the *Edinburgh* lay. She zigzagged coming out of Murmansk, steered an erratic course back and sank after veering in a wide circle in the midst of a battle. She could have gone down anywhere in some fifteen hundred square miles of ocean.

Secondly, he was told in no uncertain terms that the British government would never sanction a return to the *Edinburgh*. She had been declared a war grave in 1954, and as such was considered inviolable.

Thirdly, in any official operation, the Russians would be involved. Though the gold had been destined for America, it had been insured by Britain and the Soviet Union jointly. After the insurance was paid out by the British War Risks Insurance Office the gold – at that time valued at $6.2 million, or £1.5 million – technically became the joint property of Britain and Russia.

One thing Mike could confirm: the *Edinburgh* was in international waters. He did not wish to fight for permission to salvage the gold; nor did he wish to share the proceeds with the governments concerned. He therefore decided that, to avoid the complications of dealing with the British and Russian governments, any attempt to raise the gold would have to be a pirate operation.

It was not until 1962 that a breakthrough began to seem possible. That year Mike read an account of a twenty-six-hour stay in an underwater habitat by a Belgian, Robert Sténuit. It was clear from his experiment that his extended stay under pressure had been no more of a strain than a couple of hours would be. Moreover, the decompression time was about the same. Apparently, once a man was totally saturated with gas, it didn't matter how long he stayed down, as long as he was warm. To Mike this was something of a revelation.

Mike saw at once that if he was to remain in the forefront of technological advance he could not afford to stay in salvage. The work was simply not demanding enough.

He had no wish to work abroad. That would take him away from northern waters. It was fortunate, therefore, that the revolution for which he had been waiting occurred right on his doorstep, brought about by the discovery of North Sea gas and oil.

He made his move when gas first began to flow in 1968. He applied to a newly formed, fast-growing French company, Comex, which had just signed its first North Sea diving contracts. His experience stood him in good stead. He began diving offshore, inspecting rigs and pipes. Working in electrically heated suits, he built up experience of breathing oxygen and helium.

Helium certainly eradicated the narcs and allowed more rapid decompression from shallow depths. But in deeper dives it was like starting all over again. With helium, divers could go deeper for longer, but the problems in these untried regions were similar to those faced by compressed-air divers in the early days. No one knew how the body would react. No decompression tables existed; they had to be established by trial and error. There were no ways of coping with the strange voice distortion or the rapid loss of heat from the lung tissues.

Besides, the basic flaw in diving theory still remained. If a diver went deep – five hundred feet, say – he would still have to spend an age decompressing. Not even oil money could sustain such twisted economics.

Comex itself showed the way forward by applying the techniques developed by men like Sténuit, and also by the American 'aquanauts', who showed it was possible to live like spacemen for extended periods in an underwater habitat. No matter how long the men stayed down, it seemed they sustained no injury. And as long as the body was completely saturated with gas, decompression times needed to conform only to the depth of the dive, not to the length of stay at that depth. Theoretically, a man could work for a year at a thousand feet. Decompression might take two weeks, but in economic terms that was rendered insignificant by the length of time he had been down. Work under pressure at depth was now limited only by more tractable factors: food supply, temperature control and the diver's stamina.

It was this concept, known as 'saturation diving',

that made possible the development of North Sea oil, and also made it worthwhile to tackle the other remaining problems: how to communicate; how to counteract the cold most effectively; how to keep a diving vessel and the bell itself stable over extended periods (a sudden move horizontally or vertically might snap even the toughest cable); how to save helium after it was breathed out (at eight hundred feet, a team of divers breathed twenty-five times as much as at sea level, at a cost of up to £5000 a day); how to check on divers at work (a vital consideration, for extreme conditions could distort judgement. Question: How can you tell when a diver's lying? Answer: When his lips are moving).

Mike knew the problems well enough. In the early 1970s he found himself peculiarly well placed to assess the solutions as they emerged. For in 1972 his career as a diver came to an end. He'd known for some years that he'd been on borrowed time. At forty-six he was the oldest diver he knew. He had been working on the Glomar 3 rig. A connection broke at five hundred feet. As the most experienced man he was asked to make the repair. On the way up, the electrical heater in his suit began to malfunction. They had to bring him up fast; and then the time spent decompressing wasn't quite enough. That night there was pain in his ears and he found it difficult to keep his balance. They decompressed him again; the pain went. He remained disoriented, nothing serious, but enough for the doctor to recommend he stop diving. He became instead a diving supervisor, responsible for scheduling and controlling the dives.

As far as the *Edinburgh* was concerned, the move did not concern him unduly, other than as a sign of his own mortality. If he did put together an operation to reclaim the *Edinburgh*'s gold, he wouldn't expect to be one of the divers anyway.

About this time the focus of the diving industry shifted north, away from Yarmouth to Aberdeen, away from gas to oil. Mike moved north, too, and rented a flat near the harbour. It was here, in late 1973, after one of his reports, that Krassnik called him, the first time in nineteen years they had spoken directly.

The American wasted no time in pleasantries. The conversation was a long one, for Mike had some comments on the technical implications of what was being suggested, but in essence Krassnik's message was: 'It's time to speed up. You know what's happening to the price of gold? Going crazy. It just broke the $100 an ounce barrier. You'll see it in the papers. That changes things. Whatever the difficulties of raising that gold, we gotta go for it, and go hard. Time was, it was worth a measly $6 mill. Now it's $20 mill, and rising. Before, even if we had the technology, the project was marginal. Now we'd be into profit. You say we'll soon have the technology. OK, don't try to get ahead of the field. Let everyone else spend the research money. Then we move.

'From here on in, I wanna know the state of the game every three months, and of course any time there's a big break. I have to be in a position to make arrangements, and not just with you. I know you'll do this, Michael, because the alternatives for you would not be pleasant.'

As it happened, events played into Krassnik's hands. In the course of the next few years electronic and engineering techniques produced solutions to all the outstanding problems. Helium unscramblers knocked out the distorting upper register in divers' voices. Satellite telemetry and computer-controlled engines responding to signals from seabed beacons combined to produce 'dynamic positioning' vessels which could lock on to a spot on the surface to an accuracy of a few square yards. Complex hydraulic systems compensated for the motion of the waves, allowing diving-bells to hover motionless even while the supply ship was riding a heavy swell. In 1975 a Yarmouth company patented a diving suit heated by water pumped down from the supply ship: the water bathed the diver's body beneath his suit and flowed out at the cuffs and ankles. It became possible to recover helium and recycle it after use. Finally, in 1976, came the first remote-controlled submersible TV cameras.

During these years Mike immersed himself in

technical information and in planning. He wrote to diving companies, salvage firms, marine archaeologists and the research departments of universities and multinational companies. He scanned the literature. He subscribed to specialist magazines. He compiled price lists, schedules, budgets, manpower estimates. He devised ways of ensuring security. He became respected for his expertise, and told no one of his true ambitions.

There was one major, indeed crucial, lack: he could not specify exactly where the *Edinburgh* lay. To find her by scientific methods might take days or weeks of sonar scanning, which would add a whole new dimension to the operation. Fortunately, there was another way. It is not uncommon for trawlers to snare wrecks, especially if their exact site is uncharted.

As soon as he moved to Aberdeen, therefore, Mike had established contact with any trawler captain who had fished the Barents Sea in case their nets had tangled on any unspecified wrecks. He always explained that his reasons for wanting this information were purely personal. He bought drinks, went to the right pubs. Pretty soon his interest was known and accepted. Every few months someone would contact him with some snippet of information.

There had been plenty of reports through the 1950s and 1960s of nets snaring something that might have been the *Edinburgh*. But at that time trawlers could not record their position accurately enough and anyway there was no way of checking whether the wreck actually was the *Edinburgh*. By the 1970s, however, satellite telemetry enabled any vessels with suitable equipment – and trawlers needed such equipment to track their increasingly elusive prey – to pinpoint their position to within a few yards.

In 1978 Mike stumbled on the information he had been hoping for. He heard of it, as often, via a friend of a friend. A meeting was arranged at a pub.

The results were more than Mike could possibly have imagined.

'Nearly lost all our effing nets,' said his source, a captain, a wiry little Scot with a beard so huge it seemed to be fake. 'Funny thing, though, same thing happened a few months back a couple of miles away. We had a record of that, of course, and gave the place a wide berth. Then, bugger me, if we didn't run into this other one. Took us three hours to get clear, and cost us £1500 in repairs.'

'Big ship, was she?'

'Aye. Showed up as about six hundred feet long, once we got her clear on the sonar. At about eight hundred feet.'

Two wrecks that close – they had to be the *Hermann Schoemann* and the *Edinburgh*. Mike kept the tension out of his voice. He took a pull at his pint.

'Another, Ken?'

'Aye, I think I will.'

Mike ordered and said: 'Sounds interesting. You noted the position?'

'Aye, of course. So's we don't do the same bloody thing again.'

'Can you let me 'ave the coordinates? I'd like to try to identify the wrecks.'

'No problem. I thought you'd be wanting them.'

The trawlerman pulled a scruffy piece of paper from his anorak. On it were four sets of figures, enough for Mike to be certain that he could, with the aid of his memory, identify which was which. He'd gone over it so often in his mind: the *Hermann Schoemann* had been well west and a little south of the *Edinburgh* the last time he'd seen her.

'One thing, Ken. 'Ow many people know about this?'

'Why? Does it matter?'

'Not really. Just wondered.'

'I won't be talking, because not many people are that interested. But there's nothing secret about it, you realize. It's in the company records. We'd tell any trawlerman who asked. Besides, we're not the only ones up there. Others have snared those wrecks before; someone's bound to do it again. It'll be general knowledge within a few years, like it or not.'

'Suppose so. Thanks. One for the road?'

11

He was ready to move. But it had to be soon.

He called Krassnik in Washington on a Thursday. The return call the next day told him to be over at the weekend. He gathered his papers together, caught the evening plane to London and then booked himself on the first Washington flight on Saturday.

It was the first time he'd been to Washington, and he saw almost nothing of it. He arrived at midday and was met by a black chauffeur who took him in limousined splendour to an apartment block off Virginia Avenue. The chauffeur accompanied him in silence in the lift to the twenty-third floor.

Krassnik's Washington penthouse, with its sweeping views, was also his headquarters. There was a bedroom, a sitting room and an office with two desks, electric typewriter, telex, TV and two leather sofas. Filling one was Krassnik, who did not rise. He must have been seventy, Mike realized, but age had withered him hardly at all. The moustache was gone – too much grey perhaps – but the huge face, with its bald, domed scalp, seemed to have no more wrinkles than it had had twenty-two years previously. The flesh, still full and firm, exuded a fearful vitality. He was dressed in weekend garb – a checked sports jacket even more ample than his paunch, and a flowered shirt without tie.

'It's been a long time, Michael.' A steady stare from unsmiling eyes. 'Sit down. What do you have for me?'

As direct as ever, scary as ever.

Mike handed over his sheet of papers, the summary on the top, and tried to match the big man's authority.

'Requirements,' he said. 'Estimates. Equipment. Numbers. Proposed mode of operation.'

Krassnik grunted. He hardly glanced at the papers.

'I'll check it out later. Meantime, know the price of gold? As of yesterday, a touch over $100. Word is, that price is going up higher. Through the roof, like '73. Inflation is running high. Gold is undervalued. We could see another doubling, even trebling of its value over the next two, three years.

'I see your estimate: $4 million. A decade ago that would make the scheme no go. Right now, it looks good. Now when the price of gold skyrockets again, this haul is going to double or treble again in value. Eighty-plus million dollars for an outlay of four million? That's real business.

'But the same idea's gonna hit others. We have to

be ready first. So here's what to do. You leave your job. I pay you a regular salary: whatever you get now plus fifty per cent. I arrange an advance payment of a hundred grand to get things moving.

'I want that gold, Michael. I've wanted it since you first told me about it. And you're gonna get it for me. Do we have a deal?'

Mike paused.

'And my share?'

'Ten per cent of what you raise.'

Mike's face betrayed no emotion. But he thought: Christ, *my* gold, the gold I nearly fucking died for, and the bastard wants ninety per cent of it.

Out loud he said: 'Look, this is my big chance. An 'ole lifetime's gone into it. I've gotta come out of it with money to burn. Guarantee me a million dollars.'

Krassnik's voice went ominously quiet. The sound of it, a deep, throaty rumble, took Mike back twenty-six years, to that day when his life had hung in the balance on board the *Argo*.

'No goddamn deal. You think I'd guarantee a million when that's all you might raise? Hell, you do this right, you get your million anyway – and more. Screw it up and you pay for it. Don't try to negotiate with me, Michael. I'm telling you. And, as you well know, you have no choice in the matter.'

'OK, OK. You got your deal.' Mike raised his hands in a placating gesture. 'Just tell me one thing: is it just you I'm working for?'

Krassnik's mood switched again. He grinned. 'No. You screw this up, I'm not the only one you'll have to tangle with. I want this, and I want it bad, but I'm not about to gamble four million of my own dollars. I put up the front money, but I have backers. Let's say the economics and politics of this thing are about to escalate. And if you get out of line the world won't be big enough to hold you.'

Mike nodded resignedly. But there was no resignation inside, just a slow-burning commitment to make the salvage go his way.

12

Mike came back from his interview with Krassnik filled with conflicting emotions. He was exhilarated that at last he was moving towards the gold, yet sick at heart that he still found himself enslaved. He could see no way out of that. The alternative would have been a formal approach to the British government and – inevitably – to the Russians. Equally inevitably, this would lead either to a blank refusal of permission or complicated negotiations that would involve splitting the booty at least three ways. His share of the final pay-off might well be not much more than he would get from working with Krassnik. Whichever way he looked at it, it had to be a one-man show.

Krassnik himself set a seal on that arrangement. Within ten days $100,000 was credited to the bank account he had set up for the purpose in Guernsey. The following day, to the amazement of his UK employer, he handed in his resignation.

'Mike, we need you. Why are you doing this now?' his boss wanted to know. 'The company, the whole industry, it's going from strength to strength. You're cutting your own throat.'

'I don't think so, Jim. The company's doing well, but we both know there's no chance of me getting in on the profits.'

'So what are you going to do? Retire?'

'Something like that.'

'Come *on*! You've been in this business over thirty years. You know the problems better than anyone, and you've been part of the solutions. You know the potential. You're not trying to tell me you're just going to stop?'

'I'm not sure, Jim.'

'You mean you're not going to tell me. OK, if that's the way you want it. But just think what you're doing, man. Giving up a rock-solid, inflation-proofed income. In my book there's only one reason for doing that. You're setting up on your own.'

'I'm sorry, Jim. I can't tell you.'

Within a month Krassnik's first monthly payment – $10,000 – was credited to Mike's offshore account.

For that he would have to show some results, and soon. He became even more of a recluse, working on his own, from his flat, mainly on the phone, making comparative lists of diving support vessels, possible diving concerns, divers he knew who might be interested, helium suppliers. He asked for quotes from a number of shipping companies. He checked on depth capabilities, types of diving-bell, hot-water suits, helium unscramblers, the sophistication of various systems of dynamic-positioning equipment, the reliability of compensation mechanisms.

It was already too late to organize an expedition for the summer of 1979. To do anything during the winter was out of the question. The earliest possible opportunity was May 1980, and it was that date that he quoted.

Security was a problem. One of his closest contacts, a Norwegian named Bjørn Johannsen, whose company owned a diving support ship, told him: 'Mike, you know, there is talk. You are asking many questions. Everyone knows you want a ship and divers for a North Sea operation. Soon, if people are going to have confidence in you, you must say what your plans are.'

Had Mike been about to undertake a normal commercial operation, he would have had no hesitation in moving ahead fast. As it was, he didn't want his potential suppliers to become greedy; nor did he wish to risk official action against him But Bjørn Johannsen was different. He might be the key to the whole operation, and for that reason Mike flew to Bergen to tell him of the scheme.

Johannsen wanted to be involved. 'But,' he said, 'I don't think you can stay down long enough. You might not be able to get into the wreck. You will have to be prepared to blast her, you know?'

* * *

During this time Krassnik had also been busy. Over the previous twenty-five years he had grown extremely rich supplying arms to practically every Middle Eastern country, and was known as a businessman who served any political master who was prepared to pay him. But his true master was profit. He made that starkly clear to anybody who approached him. He was fond of stating that he would be just as willing to serve the enemies of his present paymaster. He promised only two things: arms and discretion. He never divulged information about any of his contracts. In this way he had supplied first Israel, then most countries in the Arab world with weapons from Europe, America and the Eastern bloc. It was a simple formula and it worked. He never stored any arms himself, acting only as a middleman.

Krassnik's success had brought him to the attention of Libya's new young strong man, Gaddafi, when he came to power in 1969, and in fact they had already met in Egypt when the future Libyan leader was studying in Cairo, imbibing the spirit of Arab nationalism from Nasser. Gaddafi presided over an oil-rich economy, which he promptly turned to the service of his own grandiose and fanatical designs. He saw himself as Nasser's heir and, in his determination to become sole leader of all Arabs, supported terrorists to undermine any government – including Arab ones – of which he disapproved.

Over the years Gaddafi's name had been linked with an army of terrorist organizations and a kaleidoscopic array of wild schemes. It was said that he had sent a hundred Russian rifle-propelled grenades to the Provisional IRA; armed the Black September killers of Jewish athletes at the Munich Olympics in 1972; backed the take-over of the OPEC headquarters in Vienna in 1975 (paying its perpetrator, 'Carlos', £1 million); commissioned several assassination attempts on President Sadat of Egypt; tried to overthrow the Sudanese government; offered the Tunisian Prime Minister $1 billion to allow the unification of their two countries; and sent cash and arms to Muslim revolutionaries in the Philippines. All of this he could do because he personally ran the Libyan economy and himself authorized any spending over half a million dollars. It was also said that he kept a slush fund of $1 billion simply to finance any project or group that seized his fancy.

The fact that Gaddafi was an unpredictable eccentric worried Krassnik not at all. His approach was typically direct. He was open about his own philosophy, told Gaddafi whom he might call in Saudi Arabia, Syria and Iraq to back his claims and promised to supply him with whatever he wanted.

It turned out that there was much Gaddafi wanted. He wanted fighters, transports and men to train his hit squads. He even talked grandly of acquiring nuclear capability. In 1975 he bought $500 million worth of Soviet arms – two thousand tanks and two squadrons of MiG 23 fighter planes. On the whole he, like other Middle Eastern leaders, wanted land and air weapons; but there was one other dimension to Gaddafi's ambitions: naval capability. He wanted to be able to deliver troops by sea if necessary, and was obsessed with the fear that his coast was wide open to an Israeli seaborne assault. He wanted submarines; if not nuclear submarines, then at least the best non-nuclear ones. This ambition was sharpened by an extraordinary incident in 1973.

It was the twenty-fifth anniversary of the founding of Israel. The *QE2* was on her way through the Mediterranean to Haifa with hundreds of Jews on board. There were at the time in Tripoli two Egyptian submarines on secondment to Libya. Gaddafi ordered the subs to torpedo the liner. Horrified by the order, the Egyptians cabled Sadat for confirmation, and Sadat ordered the submarines to abandon the mission and return to Egypt. Gaddafi had no other submarines capable of accomplishing the crazy scheme – a situation he swore would be remedied.

What Krassnik managed to find for him were three old but serviceable American submarines. They had been launched in 1945, escaped service in the Second World War and had then been handed to the Shah in the early 1960s. Iran was now moving on to grander things, and Krassnik took possession of the three submarines in part payment for a deal he helped to arrange in 1975 between Iran and Great Britain for the supply of Chieftain tanks. By the end of 1976 Libya possessed crews trained to run them.

Krassnik's relationship with Gaddafi went beyond that of an agent supplying arms. The *Argo* was a welcome visitor in Tripoli harbour because Gaddafi's ambitions demanded the administration of funds outside Libya. In this context Krassnik proved an ideal business partner, making no political, religious or moral judgements. On Gaddafi's behalf he established a Swiss bank account. The system they ran was a simple one. Krassnik supplied arms; Gaddafi would overpay him; Krassnik would pay the excess directly into Gaddafi's account. That money in its turn, now well laundered, could be paid to any one of a number of sources – the Baader–Meinhof Group, Basque separatists, Palestinians. There was even one payment of $100,000 to a tiny group of Austrians fighting to free the South Tyrol from Italian rule.

It was therefore quite natural that Krassnik should choose to approach Gaddafi with the scheme that Mike had presented to him.

In principle, it seemed childishly simple. The *Edinburgh* lay in international waters. Gaddafi could spare a submarine. The sub could lie undetected within easy reach of the diver's supply ship and when the gold had been collected, the sub would simply move in and take it. The diving vessel could be blasted out of the water and the divers and crew killed. The submarine, devoid of markings, would never be identified.

For an investment of $4 million, Gaddafi would receive more than $50 million worth of gold to do with as he liked. Krassnik would take twenty per cent. The gold would be transported direct from Tripoli to Zurich by a Libyan airline, sold, and the cash paid directly into Gaddafi's and Krassnik's separate accounts.

In April 1980 Mike and Johannsen undertook a preliminary survey of the area of ocean in which the *Edinburgh* had gone down. Backed by Krassnik's cash, Mike could afford a ten-day research voyage, and anyway he needed the information in order to make his arrangements. Johannsen's vessel, the *Fridtjof Nansen*, was perfect for the job – one thousand tons, with space for twenty crew and twenty-five diving personnel, a diving-bell to accommodate three divers and isolated, pressurized cabins in which they could work for several weeks before undergoing their ten days of decompression. The only piece of equipment lacking was a remote-controlled TV camera.

They were lucky with the weather. With a skeleton crew of six, it took them five days to cover the thirteen hundred miles to the bleak stretch of sea in which the *Edinburgh* had sunk thirty-eight years before. Once Johannsen had locked on to the coordinates Mike had given him, the *Fridtjof*

Nansen's sonar picked up the wreck almost at once. Even from the shadowy outline on the sonar screen, Mike could identify her.

'Oh, God,' he breathed in, staring at the shielded screen. 'Oh, God. You beauty. You bloody beauty.'

'It is her?' asked Johannsen.

'It's 'er, right enough. Can't see much detail, but she's the right length, and that stern – you see – all twisted about? Seems to be something a bit odd about the bridge . . . but she's all in one piece . . . and on 'er port side by the look of things, which means the torpedo 'ole will be uppermost. Looks good, Bjørn. Looks really good.'

'But she may be full of silt. Maybe all the bulkheads collapsed.'

'Maybe lots of things, mate. But it looks good enough to dive on to. Then if we need to we can blast 'er. But we can't tell that until we do it for real.'

It was soon after Mike's return to Aberdeen that his plan came apart at the seams. First there were the phone calls: two of them. The first was from Johannsen in Norway informing him that the *Fridtjof Nansen* would not after all be available.

'But, Bjørn. We 'ad a deal!'

'We are old friends, you and I, Mike, but . . . there is no written agreement. I remember how it was in April. I think the whole thing is crazy. I am happy to blow the ship apart, but not to have my divers work their way inside through that torpedo hole . . .'

'That's not what you said a couple of months ago, Bjørn.'

'Certain things have become clear. Mike, as a friend I say do not do this thing . . . I am sorry.'

Then the manager of the gas supply company called. Helium was going to be tricky this year. Demand from other companies in the North Sea was heavy. Touch-and-go to fulfil commitments. Nothing left over. He was afraid Mike would have to look elsewhere. Sorry.

The calls were two of a kind. There had never been any hint, when the project was first proposed, that the money wasn't right, that Mike was distrusted, that the ship and the gas might be committed elsewhere. There was enough advance warning – damn it, the North Sea was one long crisis, and any company involved was used to responding to a few hours' or days' warning, let alone a month or two.

With something like desperation, Mike began the tedious process of contacting other sources. There were few possibilities in the UK. He began to list companies in the USA, the Netherlands, West Germany.

Shortly after these conversations he learnt why his original partners had backed out. Early one morning as he leafed through the latest batch of technical pamphlets, sipping at a mug of coffee, there was a knock at the door. He opened it and saw a staid figure wearing a grey overcoat, unbuttoned to reveal a smart pinstripe suit. The man carried an umbrella over one arm, but had no briefcase. He was a little older than Mike, in his late fifties, and by the neat cut of his grey hair and his direct, blue-eyed gaze, Mike guessed he was probably a former army officer.

'Mr Cox? I wonder if I might talk to you for a few moments? My name is McBride. Ministry of Defence.'

Christ. Mike paused for a moment, shrugged, then stood aside. McBride nodded in thanks and took a seat in an armchair. He wasted no time with small talk.

'It has come to our notice that you have been showing a considerable interest in HMS *Edinburgh*. You are well known for your expertise in diving. We have also become aware that you have been contacting a number of companies with the clear intention of undertaking a diving venture of some kind. We know that you have visited the area. Clearly, given your background, you have more than an academic interest in the gold that went down with the *Edinburgh*.

'What I have to tell you is this: HMG would take it very amiss if the *Edinburgh* were touched in any way. As I am sure you are aware, she was declared a war grave in 1954. Some fifty men died in her. A war grave is not only officially sacrosanct, but it is also considered to be sacrosanct by the families of the men concerned. To desecrate a war grave would cause a pronounced sense of outrage among members of the public and among those whose job it is to protect the memory of those who died in defence of their country.'

Mike sat and stared. His secret was blown.

'If this is an official visit, you better tell me where I can reach you.'

'There's nothing official about this, Mr Cox. It cannot be an official visit, for – as you are well aware – you have not broken any law. At present, it is purely an informal request that you do not persist in your attempt to violate a war grave.' He paused, staring at Mike, feeling his resistance. 'There are, however, certain pressures that can be brought to bear.'

'For instance?'

'Come now, Mr Cox, use your imagination. Very well. HMG has a deep involvement in North Sea oil. A number of companies are absolutely dependent on sales to the government. HMG might easily look with disfavour on any company, whether British or foreign, that connccted itself with the type of operation you have been planning.'

'That explains quite a bit. You've been putting the screws on already.'

'In a couple of instances we have been able to make our feelings known, yes.'

Feelings be buggered! I suppose you'll tell me next it's got absolutely nothing to do with the fact that you and the Russians stand to lose a pile if somebody else gets in there first.'

'My dear Mr Cox, that is very much a secondary issue. The amount of gold involved would hardly be of a great national significance. No, I repeat: our major concern is a moral one. And I must tell you' – McBride raised his eyebrows and gave a wry smile – 'that if you persist, every effort will be made to stop you.'

'You threatening me?'

'Threaten, Mr Cox? I'm sure there is no need, because I can assure you that, should you persist, HMG will do all in its power to ensure that no one works with you again. And one further thought: as you know, the *Edinburgh* lies in international waters. But the Russians do not subscribe to the twelve-mile territorial limit. They claim a two-hundred-mile limit, which would place the wreck well within their area of interest. Should you pursue your venture, we may not be able to guarantee that the Soviet Union would exercise restraint.'

'Let me understand you: if we go, you'll tell the Russkies to blow us out of the water?'

'Nothing so dramatic, I hope.' McBride frowned as if pained by Mike's suggestion. 'I have no doubt they would seek to protect what they consider to be their interests in rather more subtle ways. Anyway, let me leave you to think through the implications of what I have said. I am sure you will make the right decision.'

After McBride had gone, Mike sat and thought for more than an hour. Two things were plain. The government were all out to stop him. But if he could work in secret – really in secret – there was nothing they could do directly. As McBride had said, he wouldn't be breaking any laws. If he kept tight security, HM-bloody-G wouldn't know, and wouldn't be able to tell the Russians.

OK. Just start again.

With some trepidation he reported back to Krassnik.

'Jesus,' Krassnik growled. 'The speed you're moving, we'll all be dead before we see that gold. Move your ass or I'll burn it for you.'

'I'm every bit as keen as you are, Krassnik. But I can't do anything this year. We've gotta find a boat, equipment, do another research trip – and all without anyone knowing what I'm really up to. Next May. OK?'

But he never got that far.

His efforts had been well monitored. In February 1981 he had another visit from the all-seeing McBride. This time the official was more explicit.

'Mr Cox, as I think I made clear last time we spoke, we are determined that there should be no pirate operation conducted by a British citizen on HMS *Edinburgh*. It is immoral and dangerous, and might be politically disastrous. Yet you have persisted in your efforts.

'We have therefore been forced to take action on

our own account, action I doubt you could ever have predicted. As you know, the Ministry of Defence and Secretary of State have been approached by a number of treasure seekers eager to salvage the *Edinburgh*'s gold. Each has been discouraged, as you have been. In fact, until recently, we were not concerned. She was well protected by eight hundred feet of icy water. But as you yourself have shown, that is no longer protection enough.

'We have therefore decided that the best defence is to ensure we exercise as much control as possible. We could not hope to control you; hence our opposition.

'But, at the time we had our last conversation, we were approached by a man whose understanding of the problem was impressive. He had done his homework over many years. He knew where the *Edinburgh* was and convinced us that by using saturation divers it would be possible to gain entry into the wreck without disturbing her. In brief, he created enough confidence in us – and somewhat to our surprise, in the Russians – to have himself awarded the contract to raise the gold. I can be quite frank, you see, for the contract is as good as signed. It is already an open secret. The company proposes to put its plan into effect this coming summer. When the time comes we shall be quite happy to cooperate, and to allow the venture full publicity.

'So you see, Mr Cox, there is absolutely no point

in your continuing your little scheme. Not only would you encounter formal British and Russian opposition, but by the time you arrive the gold will no longer be there.'

Throughout this speech, Mike sat in stunned silence. At the end, he said: 'Tell me who these guys are.'

'I can't do that. Of course, you can find out easily enough, because they have contracted some of the very people who might have worked with you. I don't wish to be vindictive, Mr Cox, but you're finished. Washed up.'

'Bastards.'

'Hardly, Mr Cox,' said McBride mildly. 'You did rather ask for it, didn't you?'

Mike spent a couple of hours being angry, bitter and frightened, mainly at the thought of what Krassnik might do when he found out he'd spent $250,000 for nothing. Perhaps he ought just to vanish. But then his instinct for survival imposed more rational thinking. He drank coffee and prowled his flat. He couldn't just kiss thc whole thing off, after all these years. No. First he needed to know what he was up against. Then he could respond.

McBride was right: it wouldn't take long to find out who was involved. A British company. Someone quite new, up-and-coming, aggressive, willing to take a risk. Someone like he himself might have been, if he'd had more luck.

It took a dozen calls to eliminate a few of the most obvious possibilities and track down the interloper. Ocean Pioneers. Run by a latter-day pirate, Derek Mackinsen. A tough blighter who had cut his teeth in North Sea oil operations, then branched out into treasure-hunting, and done very well for himself, filling his Aberdeen mansion with a museum of artefacts hauled up from wrecks all over the world.

Mike called him.

There was just the briefest of pauses when he put the question, and then: 'I can say quite categorically that we have not proposed any such scheme to the government.'

There was something about the formality of the denial that made him suspicious. He phoned one of the Ocean Pioneers divers and told him of his own scheme and of McBride's visit.

'You see, Dick,' he concluded, 'it's practically in the open anyway. Otherwise I wouldn't 'ave been warned off. You won't be giving much away. My guess is it's Ocean Pioneers. True?'

Then he had it. The outline of the consortium – a young businessman named as the originator of the idea and the consortium; Ocean Pioneers to handle diving; the Bremen-based Offshore Supply Association to provide the diving support ship, *Stephaniturm*; Racal Decca Survey Ltd supplying hydrographic equipment. The survey, of course, already tied up. The operation timed for August.

Huh. If that lot were all in on a profit-sharing basis, it was no more than a good business deal. No one party was going to get away with the lot.

Britain and Russia would want their cut. That wasn't the way to do it.

He'd have to move fast. Stateside. Match the Ocean Pioneers consortium, using Krassnik's money.

He called Krassnik.

After warning him of bad news to come, he went on: 'There's another bunch of people going for the gold with full government backing. We guessed it might happen. Now it has. I've been warned off by an MoD stooge. Word of what I was up to must have got out. As far as I'm concerned, our plan's dead. But I . . .'

'If it's dead, so are you. Think again.'

'Jesus, I've thought. I'm thinking. I . . .'

'No choice, Michael,' Krassnik interrupted. 'I'm up to my neck in this thing. I can't afford to let it go, either financially or politically.'

'Well, I'm sorry. I really am. I've been trying to pull this stunt together for years, and then the ground is cut away from under my feet. It's fuckin' ironic really, because I know some of the blokes going.'

This remark seemed to spark off something in Krassnik's mind.

'You do, huh?' He paused meditatively. 'Answer me this. Any chance you could get on that boat?'

'The *Stephaniturm*? Dunno. Look pretty funny, suddenly coming out of retirement like that.'

'But you have a good deal to offer, no? Perhaps you could get yourself a job on board?'

The idea appealed to Mike. 'Yeah, that'd be pretty bloody amazing, to be on the boat and watch the gold being raised. But where do you come in?'

'My plans are no concern of yours. Your job is to help retrieve the gold.'

'You planning an 'ijack? Christ, you crazy? You know the conditions up there? Even in summer it's freezing. And there's bound to be some protection, what with the . . .'

Krassnik's voice hardened. 'I said my plans need not concern you. What I'll need from you is action, and information. Stay on the end of a phone. I'll call later.'

The call came in the early hours.

'OK. Between us, we can get this gold, Michael. We'll get to the details later, but at present there's only one question I have to ask. Assuming you can get on that boat, could you send a message – any message – from on board?'

Mike thought, and then explained. Normally there wouldn't be a problem. Communication is a matter of life and death aboard a vessel like that. She would have a radio that could speak direct to the home base, be patched into the telephone network, or print out the communication as a telex. 'But I've been over this ground already, time after time,' he insisted. 'It's not a question of whether she's got the equipment or not. It's a question of whether she'll be handling information in clear rather than coded. I imagine that even with British and Russian approval, they'll be pretty keen to keep things secret.'

'But they'll be in contact with their home base?'

'For sure.'

'In that case it will be up to you to devise a way of getting a message through.'

'Wait a minute. I'm not even on the bloody ship yet.'

'Get to work. It's in your own interests, Michael, because this is your last chance to get a share of that gold. I know where it is. I will get it, with or without your help. So move.'

On his return Mike contacted Ocean Pioneers. They told him to send in a job application. He reviewed his background, said he wanted work as a diving supervisor, pointed out his qualifications and also wrote of his own personal involvement with the *Edinburgh*. 'I'm the only man in the country,' he explained, 'who is both an *Edinburgh* survivor and a diver.'

He delivered the letter by hand.

Later the same day he received a phone call. There was no post on the *Stephaniturm* to match his qualifications. The only unfilled job was as a deck supervisor, looking after the raising of any finds. He'd get nothing more than a living wage

– £80 per day, no bonuses – but if he wanted the job, he was welcome to it.

For the sake of his dignity, he said he'd call back. But he had already made his decision. He'd go.

13

He phoned Krassnik.

'I thought you'd find a way,' said the American. 'This is the plan . . .'

He needed two, and only two, pieces of information. He would want to know when the boat departed from base and when enough gold had been raised to make a snatch worthwhile. At the present price of gold it wouldn't need so many bars.

'To be safe,' he added, 'let's say I want that signal as soon as you've lifted twenty bars.'

'What am I in for?'

'Five per cent of anything over twenty bars.'

'Jesus, you trying to cut my throat?'

'That's the deal. If all the gold is raised, you still stand to make $4 million. Take it or leave it.'

Mike knew he had no choice, and agreed.

'Fine,' said Krassnik. 'Now take down this address. Apartment 9a, 21 Albemarle Street, London W1. No name. What you do is ask your company for a personal favour – they gotta look after the families of the crew and divers, right? So what you do is get them to call a flower company and have them send a single rose to that address. Make it credible – dictate a card as if to a girlfriend. OK?'

'Suppose so. What's this address you've given me?'

'Don't worry about that. And don't try to go there – it's empty.'

'Is that it? What am I getting into?'

'The less you know, the safer we are, and the more certain it is that you get your share. Don't ask questions. Just do your part and we'll all be rich.'

A hijack.

How in God's name would Krassnik arrange to hijack a ship in the Russian Arctic?

One thing was certain: neither the British nor the Russians planned on doing much to counteract such a threat. There was no attempt at providing security. Mike had a conversation about this with one of the diving supervisors, who told him why.

'It's not all that surprising,' came the reply. 'It'd be expensive – the British and the Russians would spend all the income in advance protecting us lot. Then the only people who'd make any money out of it would be us, the salvors. Far better to let us take the risks and they can share in the profits for nothing. Besides, who's going to give us any trouble? It's only just been announced that we're going, and the coordinates haven't been made public. And think of the conditions, the difficulty of finding us and the fact that we're only just off the Russian coast anyway. Seems safe enough to me.'

But Mike knew different.

In his imagination he gave himself unlimited funds and began to plan what he would do if he had to hijack the gold. He fantasized an airborne attack. That way, you had range and speed. A helicopter assault would be best. Might be possible to get a chopper fitted with long-range fuel tanks to take it from the Norwegian coast to the *Stephaniturm*, put a few commandos aboard, blast the gold store, stack it in a cargo net and escape – all before the Russians or anyone else had time to send help.

Of course, there would then be the problem of shipping the gold southwards. But that coast was so wild and uninhabited that a well-organized team could vanish. They could easily have a transport plane ready to fly south, even have a ship nestling in one of the fiords. With a little forewarning – and God knows Krassnik had had that – anything was possible.

But planes were visible and vulnerable. They would be probing the northern flanks of both Western and Russian defences. Same with ships – at least the sort of vessels needed to mount a hijack. No, what would be needed would be something hidden, and reliable.

A sub. Of course. These waters were the natural haunt of submarines. Had been forty years before, and still were now.

So that would be it: a sub rising from the depths, a quick attack, slip off silently with the gold, and away to some safe and distant harbour, where he would be free to take his share and hop it.

His share. That was the bit he didn't like. He had risked his life once, and dedicated many years since to this gold, and he was damned if he could see why he should arrange to hand over $80 million worth, yet receive only four million quid for his efforts. And there was no guarantee of getting even that. Who knew how much would be raised? Who knew how much Krassnik would let him have?

The more he thought about it, the more angry he became – at himself, and at Krassnik. He remembered how he had been treated. He remembered Sandra, all those years ago. He remembered the years of frustration and impotence.

And he remembered the *Edinburgh*, replaying his former life as if he were about to die. She was a war grave. His mates were down there, along with his vanished childhood. She was herself a body, the bones of a society in miniature. What right did Krassnik, or fucking foreigners, have muscling in on gold that he and hundreds of other British sailors, and now British divers, had risked and lost their lives for?

Come to think of it, why would the bastard need to have *him* alive? He'd said he could do the job without him. As long as he was alive he'd be a risk. He knew too much. Why then let the boat, the crew, the divers survive?

The more he thought about it, the more sense it made. Simplest thing would be to take the gold and kill everyone. Yes. That was it, that was *it* . . . What had Krassnik said? He didn't need Mike . . . needed him only to raise the gold . . . so there would be no need to keep him alive. Or the crew.

Christ, the bastard was planning not just a hijack, but murder. Having him on the *Stephaniturm* was just a neat way of getting the guidance he wanted, then killing him off, along with the rest. No need to share. No need to risk identification. Just take the gold, sink the boat, kill everyone on board and run.

He had to stop Krassnik.

But how? He could simply go to the authorities with his information. And say what? That he was almost sure an American arms dealer was on the point of organizing a hijack in the Barents Sea? With a submarine? Whose submarine? Where was his evidence?

No. That would be almost as self-destructive as doing nothing. They would want to know all about his involvement with Krassnik. Much of that had been on the borders of legality, sometimes way over. If they didn't believe him, they would at least detain him. If they believed him, they would cancel the whole venture and then there would be no gold at all, for anyone.

There had to be a better way, a way to seize control of his own destiny, and perhaps also secure for himself a proper reward for the years of slavery to one man.

He began to construct a scenario that would lead to guaranteed freedom and wealth. His options were few. To retain control, and do so with some hope of a decent reward, he had to comply with Krassnik's orders, allow the salvage to go ahead, be on the vessel and make whatever arrangements he could to guarantee his position.

What were his assets? Only knowledge, the near certainty that if gold was raised it would never make it back to land. There would have to be a deal, of course. His information, such as it was, in exchange for a share of the gold. But once he had imparted that information, he would be impotent again, with nothing to prevent a double-cross.

He needed back-up, something that would give him some clout.

Nursing a whisky in his flat, he saw with sudden clarity the only possible way forward.

He needed his own private army. Perhaps not an army, but at least a group that would be ready to move faster than anyone else could possibly move, a group trained in combat at sea, a group that had access to dinghies, arms, limpet mines, radios, stun-grenades, parachutes; a group that would be ready to leave in minutes.

He needed people like those he had known in

the war, or rather their latter-day counterparts. He had had enough contact to know he could talk to them about it, because for fifteen years after the war there had been the annual get-together with the lads who had been on the Mandracchio raid. But in fact the only one whose number he still had was Andy Cunningham, who had become a banker and was now something very grand in the City. Twice in the past five years, on London visits, Mike had called, been welcomed, invited for a drink after work; and once Cunningham had come to Aberdeen – something to do with oil investments – and the two of them had met at the bar of the airport hotel. Andy would help, if he could.

It took two calls: one brief to establish contact and pose the problem, and a longer one to lay the plan.

Yes, Andy Cunningham was in touch with the Marines and the current high command of the SBS. Yes, he would make the introductions and vouch for Mike. But he couldn't have any further involvement, couldn't be seen to be a force behind such a wild, improbable venture. 'Love to, Mike, you know that. Hint of the old days. But details will be strictly up to you.'

Then came the contact itself. A senior Marine officer whose name he never knew called. Mike explained the problem, and its peculiar status, with all its uncertainty.

'So you see, sir' – strange that he, a middle-aged

man, should feel like a young corporal again – 'if this turns out the way I think, the ship is going to need help, fast.'

'Let me get this straight. You're asking me to plan for rapid deployment to the Arctic of a force of – what? Twenty? Let's say twenty men – who, on your say-so, will fly fifteen hundred miles to the area in time to forestall a hijack and seize this hypothetical submarine.'

'Yes.'

A long pause.

'It's the craziest thing I've ever heard. But let's think it through. For one thing, your line of communication would be through the company to government, not to me direct. So we would be responding to the MoD. That's as it should be. Next, it may never happen, so I can't authorize much pre-emptive action. Just an informal stand-by operation. Interesting, Cox.'

Then a sudden decisiveness. 'You know, we're always looking for scenarios that will test us. Some of us have trained in the Arctic. Canoes, that sort of thing. Never know when you might have to sort out trouble in some God-forsaken place.'

Finally: 'Very well. Leave it to me. Can't tell you what will be done, but take it we'll be standing by. One thing: if anything happens, tell your superiors to contact us. They know how.'

Mike saw the *Stephaniturm* for the first time when he joined her in Peterhead.

She was a gem of a vessel: fourteen hundred tons, two hundred and twenty-four feet long, twenty officers and crew, and up to thirty-seven diving and maintenance personnel. Full dynamic positioning with one stern propeller or 'thruster', two bow thrusters and a transverse thruster. Eight watertight compartments. Four generators and emergency batteries. A workshop. An A-frame hoist on her stern that could lift sixty tons. She was as tightly packed with electronic equipment as a space capsule – radar, radio direction finder, gyro compasses, autopilot, echograph, Decca Navigator, a main transmitter and an emergency transmitter, two main receivers and on emergency receiver.

All of this was to service the ship's real heart – the diving-bell and the chamber, a separate universe in which the divers could live, eat and sleep under pressure for weeks. From their chambers they could transfer to the half-ton diving-bell, which would then be lowered from the ship's hollow core – the 'moon pool' – to up to thirteen hundred feet below the surface of the sea. In the bell the divers could don their hot-water suits, supplied with water, gas and communications lines by an umbilical cord from the bell, open a hatch in the floor and let themselves through into the dark, cold Arctic waters. They would take with them lights and a video camera, to check that the wreck really was the *Edinburgh* and then to monitor their progress.

There were two main command structures. One line of organization saw to the running of the ship – captain, first mate, engineers, navigators, cooks, deck-hands and mess boys. The other division took care of the diving. A diving superintendent, nominally responsible to the captain, oversaw two diving supervisors, four life-support technicians, four electrical and mechanical technicians, four tenders, and then – in the chamber complex itself – the six divers. Between them the divers would work round the clock in eight-hour shifts, with two men on duty in the depths. Of these two, one would be in the bell, the other at the end of his umbilical cord in the *Edinburgh*.

As deck supervisor, Mike shared his work – which was mainly to oversee the working of the A-frame – with another deck supervisor. The two men each had control of a deck foreman and deck crew.

Finally, in addition to Mike and his small team, those on board were to include an enigmatic figure from the MoD, two stolid Russians, a journalist and a film cameraman.

In contrast to Mike's own operation, this one was mounted with the full approval of the British and Russian governments. By the terms of the agreement, the salvors were to take forty-five per cent of the gold, and of the remainder, the British were to have one-third and the Russians two-thirds, in accordance with the risks as defined by the original insurance policy. The salvors had undertaken that every effort would be made to cause as little disturbance as possible to the site, and if any human remains were found they were to be buried at sea.

To reach such an agreement with such recalcitrant partners was a political master-stroke. But it was no guarantee of success. No one had done wet-suit saturation diving at that depth. There had been deeper dives – the record at that time was about two thousand feet, but that had been in the safety of a research chamber complex. Moreover, the conditions made the whole operation extremely risky. Anything, everything, could go wrong. The weather could make the dive impossible. They might not find the wreck again. The divers might not get into her. They might not even find the gold.

14

The journey to the Arctic began when the *Stephaniturm* left Peterhead without escort on 20 August.

Mike fulfilled the first part of his instructions without trouble. The telexed request was accepted and relayed along with a dozen other messages, all personal communications of some kind. Some of the crew even followed his example and ordered flowers. Mike's was dispatched and forgotten as soon as it was sent: a single red rose to the Albemarle Street address, via Interflora, bearing the bland message: 'All well, darling. See you soon.' The only comment was from the communications officer: 'Wife, Mike?'

'Girlfriend.'

'Bastard,' the man said, with a wink, assuming Mike was married and having an affair.

In technical terms the trip was thoroughly routine. During the last few days of the eight-day journey, all six divers were 'pressed down' to a pressure equivalent to a depth of eight hundred feet, breathing their special combination of oxygen and helium at a pressure of 350lb per square inch.

Mike had virtually nothing to do except to review his own job in detail. The gold, if found, would be raised in a metal cage by the A-frame, be received by him, checked at once by the representatives of the British and Russian governments, carried to a small room that had been specially fitted with three locks – one for the salvors, one for the British and one for the Russians – and locked in. Each delivery would be meticulously recorded.

The Russians in particular were obsessed with security. They were clearly concerned that the divers themselves might be in a position to secrete bars of gold that would never appear on the official manifest. There were a number of conferences to convince them that there was no chance of such a thing. With TV cameras monitoring progress both outside and inside the diving-bell, inspection of the bell after the operation was finished and personal supervision of each bar as it went into its locked cupboard, the idea of theft was ridiculous.

Mike kept a deliberately low profile, though everyone knew of his experience on board the *Edinburgh*. He was called in on conferences to advise on how the divers might approach the bomb-room. He looked at videos of the torpedo hole. He pored over detailed plans of the *Edinburgh*.

There were a number of unknowns. The bomb-room had been flooded at the time of the explosion, but how big a hole had been blasted in that particular bulkhead? After all, Peaches had died slowly, because his little cabinet had been watertight. Mike hazarded a guess that there would be a way straight through into the bomb-room. But it could be full of all sorts of shit. Bomb-room, fuel tank, damage control room, mess deck, four-inch magazine, perhaps even the wireless cabinet itself after all these years, could all be open to the sea. The gold might be there and safe all right, but buried so deep it would take an age to find any of it.

All this was the subject of numerous conversations, and it merged into a communal obsession about how much gold there was down there and how much each man was going to get out of it. The divers, for instance, were risking not just their lives but their financial standing. This was a 'no cure, no pay' contract, for which their earnings could range from nothing to £4000 per week. Everyone aboard became an expert in the fluctuating price of gold. Aberdeen relayed the prices daily, along with exchange rates. Conferences and meals ended in a litter of scraps of paper covered in scribbled estimates of the booty's worth.

Mike, of course, also had his own set of inner tensions to cope with. He constantly played out the many possible dramas in prospect should the gold be lifted. These included the hijack (what if he had guessed wrong? what if Krassnik had some other scheme in mind?) and the rescue (his information blocked, or the SBS delayed by bad weather). If anything went wrong he could expect at best poverty, more probably death.

He also found his mind increasingly taken up with the memory of the *Edinburgh* and his experiences of almost forty years earlier. Every night, several times, he relived the lurch of the explosion, the feel of the oily floor, the sudden fear that he was touching blood in the darkness, the sight of the buckled stern, the last conversation with the sleepy, dying Peaches, and the *Edinburgh*'s slow glide into the depths, interrupted only by that brief little curtsey. He thought about his own escape, about how easily he might have been one of those buried down there. He wondered what had happened to Peaches' body. There shouldn't be much left of the bodies; they'd all be broken up, and the bones probably decalcified. Anyway, as Mike himself pointed out, there shouldn't be any bodies actually in the bomb-room, unless they had somehow drifted in there afterwards. Old Peaches, God bless him, should still be firmly encased in the wireless cabinet.

Meanwhile Krassnik's arrangements with Gaddafi were following their own course.

The Albemarle Street flat was rented on a monthly basis, at an exorbitant rate, by the Libyan Embassy in London, or rather the 'People's Bureau', as Gaddafi styled it. It had been used several times by Libyan agents planning to wreak 'revolutionary vengeance' on a few Libyans who had chosen to ignore their unpredictable leader's order to return. Most of the time the place remained empty. In the second week of August, however, it was reoccupied.

Then, shortly before midday on the twenty-second, the Interflora agent in nearby Berkeley Square delivered a single red rose to the flat. The messenger was an eighteen-year-old student doing a summer job. He got an abrupt reception. The door was opened quickly by a dark-skinned, middle-aged man in sunglasses.

'Is this . . . ?' was all the student had time to say, for the occupant simply grunted, 'Yes,' took the cellophane-wrapped flower and slammed the door.

The student thought it a little odd that the sentimental gift should have been so obviously expected, and the recipient's curt behaviour struck him as peculiar. But, with several more calls to make before lunchtime, he dismissed it from his mind and returned to the van parked outside. He had another delivery to make not far away in Dover Street, and so was in time, on his return past the block, to see the same man hurrying out of the building.

The Libyan was going to the People's Bureau, from where he made two telephone calls: one to Tripoli, the other to Washington.

That afternoon an unmarked American submarine slipped out of Tripoli harbour and headed west.

A mile out to sea, she dived, then proceeded at a steady eighteen knots. Two days later she slipped through the Strait of Gibraltar. There was no sonar to record her progress, but the USA, working as part of NATO, had long since positioned microphones at regular intervals on the seabed to pick up the noise of any passing nuclear submarine. Computers in Gibraltar were programmed to match any noise to the sound-print of any one of a hundred nuclear submarines of which NATO had a record. The sound of this particular submarine fitted no known pattern, and came only briefly to the attention of the duty officer. He guessed it was either Italian or Israeli, and gave it no further thought.

The sub proceeded northwards for seven days, surfacing daily to recharge its batteries by switching to diesel, and covering five hundred miles a day. She passed well west of Ireland and approached the Arctic through the Orkney Gap. Again the sound of engines was recorded. Again it was ignored: so many submarines passed to and fro in the icy waters south of the Faroes that only Russian nuclear subs were officially logged. The rest – especially the old conventional ones – were assumed to be of Scandinavian origin.

The Libyan submarine, travelling almost twice as fast as the *Stephaniturm*, arrived at the designated spot, a hundred and twenty miles north of Murmansk, a full day ahead of her prey. She was able to trace both the *Edinburgh* and the

Hermann Schoemann in good time, and slipped down alongside the German wreck. There she was utterly safe: no sonar could separate her image from that of the *Hermann Schoemann* and, with engines silent, no microphone, however sensitive, would have picked her up.

There she lay, awaiting the signal that would tell her the *Stephaniturn* contained sufficient gold to make an attack worthwhile. Then she would be free to pick her time. Her captain had been told to use his own initiative. He had also been promised a percentage of the booty, and the longer the *Stephaniturm* worked, the more there would be for him. He had therefore made his decision: if the weather did not force his hand he would attack only when she headed for Murmansk.

Meanwhile he and his crew had nothing to do but wait.

The *Stephaniturm* arrived above the *Edinburgh* on Thursday 3 September. The ship's computers kept her fixed in position, ensuring that once the diving-bell was lowered it would drop exactly above the *Edinburgh*.

Early on Friday morning the bell was lowered from the ship's moon pool. There were three men on board on that first dive, but they found the space in the bell too constricting and decided from then on to work in pairs.

Then, for the next few days, there followed the

slow exploration and penetration of the hull itself. There were numerous minor snags – hot water failed to circulate properly through the suits, a heat exchanger leaked, the camera threatened to foul its own cables. A couple of times divers scalded themselves in their own hot water. There were several cases of headaches, motion sickness, stomach upsets and ear infections. For a week Mike supervised the retrieval of the debris, among which was a piece of steel plate measuring three feet by two feet six inches – it was received on board as if it were the very door to the bomb-room – and a good deal of live ammunition. The shells were defused and the rest was stacked in a container on the stern of the ship.

Only after about two weeks' work was it possible for the divers to enter the bomb-room.

At that time, late on 16 September, Mike was off duty in the diving control room, listening to the conversation on the intercom and watching the muddy pictures from below. He had a feeling that if the gold was in the bomb-room at all, the divers were about to get it. He was therefore part of the group that were the first to learn that it had been found.

It was hard to see anything at all in the silt kicked up by the divers' activities, despite the powerful arc lights set up inside the hull. A twenty-seven-year-old diver called Rossier was lifting small bits of metal into the basket, working by touch. One piece of metal felt uncannily smooth beneath his rubber gloves. He raised it: it was very heavy. At that moment he knew he had succeeded. He lifted the bar slowly up to the level of his face-plate, then shouted, 'I've found the gold! I've found the gold!' In his exhilaration he executed a sort of slow-motion dance of joy, reminding those watching on the TV monitor of the blurry jumping astronaut they had seen during the first moon landing.

At once, others on board heard his shout and took up the cry. Men came running from the mess decks, a couple of them upsetting a game of Scrabble in their haste.

Though Mike was not technically on duty, he wanted to see the raising of the first bar of gold, and went out under the arc lights on the stern to watch the cage being lifted by the A-frame.

As the cage broke surface, and he saw the bar glinting dully amidst the other debris from the bomb-room, he found himself in tears. Suddenly, in his imagination, with the wind whistling all around him and the lights glaring above him, he was back on the damp deck of the *Edinburgh* watching the crane lift up the first few crates of gold from the barge beneath.

'Come on!' someone shouted. 'Let's have it!'

The supervisor on duty heaved out the bar and stood there testing the weight of it in his hands, before passing it round. No one had thought of capturing the significance of the moment, no one had anything but cliché to express their reactions. God, they said, it's heavy. One of the Russians said with stolid formality that this was a historic moment.

Everyone was photographed holding the bar. Then it was shown to the off-duty divers through the tiny porthole of their pressurized chamber and locked away.

There was little sleep that night, for bar followed bar minute by minute, at £100,000 a time. Throughout the following day Mike supervised the raising of the gold, with only brief pauses as the divers burrowed into a new pile of silt, took time out to handle ammunition or changed shifts.

When his shift ended, at six p.m., he had lost count of the number of bars he had handled. A glance at the manifest held by the watching officials reminded him: one hundred and twenty. More than enough to make Krassnik's attack worthwhile. More than enough, if he could guarantee even a minuscule royalty, to keep him in luxury for the rest of his life.

Now was thc time to slip down to the communications room and request permission to send a telex. He hesitated briefly. What if no message was received? Almost certainly it would make no difference. Having come so far, whoever was in command would not simply return empty-handed.

'I have to have it checked,' said the officer on duty. 'Blackout for anything remotely sensitive. Even then, we have to use code, so keep it short. We're not ready yet to risk announcing anything publicly. Otherwise the journalist chappies would go berserk, right?'

'Well,' said Mike, 'this is personal. Same as before.' He grinned. 'I'm getting on. I can't afford to let a young chick like this think I've forgotten her, see?'

So his request was sent: a single red rose to go to 9a, 21 Albemarle Street, London W1, with a card reading simply 'Love, Mike'.

15

For the next two weeks work proceeded more routinely. Down below, the divers, with their supply lines snaking out through the hole in the bomb-room bulkhead up to the bell twenty feet above the hulk, wrestled their way past heavier debris – ammunition trolleys and a compressor, lying in sediment still thick with oil. Often it was hard for the divers to identify what they were loading into the cage along with the gold. It was part of Mike's job to sort through these odd, slimy pieces of debris. Once he found a couple of human bones, femurs, which were buried with due ceremony. Someone he had known? Old Jim Goodall, whose body had drifted out through the hole? Sometimes he came across a four-inch shell, possibly one he himself had handled during his time on the *Edinburgh*.

His mind was therefore constantly in two worlds – present and past; up here and down there. Even while he cast an eye at the horizon, wondering when Krassnik's helicopter was going to turn up, he would be reminded of the times the German reconnaissance planes appeared over those same horizons.

He found each load would jog his memory, so that images of himself as a boy seaman surged up from his subconscious in a random sequence. Whenever he lifted a bar he could hear Peaches' awed murmur 'Cor!' He lost count of the times he thought of the chief and his 'Russian gold dripping with blood'. 'Bloody gold . . . not what a fighting ship's for . . . not trying to nick it, Cocky . . . want the truth, son? . . . deserves his tot like the rest of us!'

Nevertheless he was totally unprepared for what came out of the cage on Saturday 3 October. Memory could have played no part in predicting it, and indeed would have rejected it as impossible. But in that confined space in the *Edinburgh*, stirred randomly for thirty-nine years by the Arctic currents, any particular combination of objects became a possibility.

This time the cage came up twisted in its cable. It must have caught on the hull as it was hauled through. The crane operator swung the A-frame and the cage, pouring water, swung down to the deck. The cable seemed to be knotted strangely over the cage's door. Inside were several bars and the pile of oily debris.

'Best cut it,' said Mike. 'Then get another cage down to them.'

A blowtorch arrived from the workshop. It was Mike himself, watched by the usual team of bureaucrats, who cut the strands of the mesh cage. When the square of the mesh was almost clear, he shouted to his foreman to raise the cage a few inches. Mike gripped it and jerked at the cut section, which bent towards him. The cage tipped, the contents shifted and then, in a sudden rush oiled by the slimy sediment, spewed out on the deck at his feet. He saw half a dozen bars of gold, some .303 cartridges, fabric of some kind, a good deal of mud and a little dark circle that looked like a coin.

Mike picked up the first bar and, as he usually did, brushed the dirt away with his glove to glimpse the number.

It was his: KP 1926.

''Ere,' he said. 'This is the bar I 'eld.' He grinned round at the crowd that had pressed in upon him. Someone patted his shoulder. 'My bar,' he repeated. 'My bar.'

Indeed the bar was bound to come up eventually, and there was a fifty-fifty chance of Mike receiving it. But what happened next was more remarkable. After handing the bar on, Mike reached down to the little coin-like object. As he raised it he saw it had a chain attached to it. It was not a coin, but a British Navy identity disc. Mike held it between finger and thumb, rubbed away the silt and held it to catch the light. It was badly corroded, but still legible: 'Derek Hoskins. 36798.'

He stared for a long time, saying nothing.

Everyone was watching him, waiting for him to

reach for the next bar. Instead he went on staring at the little disc.

'What is it, Mike?' said his foreman.

'Peaches. Bloody Peaches. My mate. It's 'is dog-tag. Derek 'Oskins. But 'ow could 'e . . . ?'

Somehow the disc had drifted out of the wireless cabinet and down into the bomb-room.

'Come on, Mike. Get on with it.'

'No, 'ang about. This is odd. 'Ave I missed something? Perhaps I was asleep. Was there any mention any time of the wireless cabinet door?'

'What's he on about? Mike, for Pete's sake, let's move this gold.'

'All right, all right.' He forced himself back to the present, and turned to the MoD man. 'I want this. Can I have it?'

The man frowned. 'Really I should . . . this is a war grave . . . the family . . .'

'Yeah, I know. But look – 'e was my mate. I stayed with 'is family. I'll find them better than anyone, if there's any of them left.'

'Very well.'

After that Mike returned to work. But his mind was elsewhere. He'd already begun to devise a plausible explanation.

Peaches must have woken again. He'd found the phone link cut off. Perhaps he'd panicked. The only way out would have been through the watertight door. Water was leaking underneath. But he'd previously heard cries on the other side.

He must have forced up the handles. The water would have begun to pour in faster, balancing the pressure and easing his task. Then, with the air foul around him, and icy water up to his waist, the last catch must have given. Peaches hadn't suffocated at all. He'd been drowned, and in ensuring his own death in this fashion he'd opened a way, via damage control, to the bomb-room itself. He had died, as he wanted, touching the gold. It might even have been his bones that Mike had seen consigned to the deep several days before.

The theory thus elaborated over the next few hours was mixed in his mind with other memories. The tag. He'd forgotten all about old Peaches saying it was 'like writing on his grave'. It was as if he'd known there was a sub waiting to get them. Those subs, lurking like cold-water sharks, lurking like Krassnik's sub now.

Suddenly, what with the memories and the tag and the bones and burial, the *Edinburgh* became more than a treasure store.

By then the gold had been emerging from the depths regularly for two weeks. How long had it taken his message to be received and relayed? How long before the hijack itself? How long, in fact, did he have to save his own life and the lives of all the others? Possibly, if he was lucky, until the *Stephaniturm* left the *Edinburgh*. But what if the weather deteriorated and they had to leave prematurely? Or if the Libyans decided to cash in on what had been raised already?

He chose to move at the end of his next day's duty.

He asked for a private interview with the captain, a German called Werner Kohlmeyer, a bulky, clean-shaven man of fifty-two whose utter professionalism had won him the respect of all the Englishmen on board. The only comment Mike had heard from his was when he came in to see the TV-monitor pictures of the torpedo hole. Kohlmeyer had nodded and said with a smile: 'That is quite a hole!' His English was very good, with only a hint of an accent. 'We made damn good torpedoes!'

In Kohlmeyer's well-appointed office on the forecastle deck on the port side, the two men sat on the corner sofa. Kohlmeyer was leaning back. Mike was hunched forward over the circular, plastic-covered coffee table. He was confident enough of his decision, but all too well aware of how crazy he would sound, of the difficulty of carrying conviction, of the impact his words would have once he was believed.

'I . . . I have some information that is vital to the future of the gold and everyone on this vessel,' he began.

The captain frowned. 'Yes?'

'The *Stephaniturm*'s about to be 'ijacked.'

Kohlmeyer gave a wry smile.

'Oh, come on, Mr Cox – Mike, may I call you Mike? Hijacked? Out here?'

'It's no joke. There's a bunch of people waiting out

there right now. I must ask you to contact Aberdeen right away and ask for 'elp.'

'Help? This is really ridiculous. What help? Against what? Who?'

'I'm ready to tell you . . . but I want something in return. And for that you'll 'ave to contact Aberdeen. And London. And Moscow.'

Kohlmeyer nodded, but still forced a smile.

'Mike. This is really very amateur. Are you yourself a hijacker, perhaps, and you wish to hold us all to ransom? A foolish joke, if I may say so . . .'

'I'm quite serious, sir.'

'Then you are crazy. You think I should take you seriously? You say you're part of an attempt to hijack . . .'

'It ain't me, sir. I'm not organizing it. But I did 'ave a role to play. I know what I'm talking about. I'm cut in on the share of the proceeds. But now I want to tell you about it, and stop it.'

'Then please' – there was no smile left on Kohlmeyer's face – 'do so.'

'Not yet. As I said, I need to have a guarantee of my own security afterwards, I need enough money to last me and I need my freedom.'

'You are serious.' But Mike could see he was still being humoured. 'I have to understand,' the captain went on, as if playing for time. 'Why don't you let them go ahead?'

'I got to thinking. I was told I'd be all right. I was

told you'd all be all right, too. But now I'm not so sure. I don't want to take that risk. They could just as easy blow this ship out the water.'

'I see. Rather late to think about that, is it not?'

'Look, we're in a rush. I'll tell you the details and someone's got to take action. You'll 'ave to talk to Aberdeen, and a whole lot of people in Britain and Russia will 'ave to talk to each other. See, I've been living this for weeks now. There is an organization back 'ome ready to help. But we've got to get the information through first. Now. So can we get on with the business?'

Now Kohlmeyer was beginning to waver. 'I don't know if I believe you. If you are not telling me the truth we have no business.'

Mike's frustration suddenly became too much for him. 'Of course I'm telling the bloody truth! You think I'd risk my position 'ere, my whole professional life, just for some sick joke? Look, you can't afford *not* to believe me.' His anger, his obvious conviction, broke through the last of Kohlmeyer's reluctance to act.

The captain nodded.

'Besides,' Mike added quietly, 'you've got nothing to lose by 'earing me out. Everything to lose if you don't.'

'All right. Tell me this crazy thing.'

'As I said before, not so bloody quick. I want a guarantee first.'

'Yes?'

'Ten bars of gold.'

'Ten bars?' Kohlmeyer's eyes widened and he shrugged. 'We would all like ten bars of gold. You think that's possible with English and Russian officials here?'

'That's exactly why you need to make contact. Everyone must agree. But I've not finished. I want a direct flight to Zurich from Murmansk. A new passport and a new name, issued there. I want to vanish. I 'ave to. My life will depend on it. Now, for God's sake, let's move. If there's an attack now, or at dawn, and I've told you, and nobody's taken any action . . .'

'All right. True, I have nothing to lose. After all, if there is no hijack . . .'

'Right. So move.'

'This is not so easy. We must speak in code. The communications officer must know.'

'So tell him, if that's what it takes.'

Both men paused. Then Kohlmeyer made his decision.

'Very well.' He pushed an intercom button and asked the communications officer, Jerry Finlay, to join him.

When Finlay arrived, Kohlmeyer explained the situation. As he spoke, Mike avoided Finlay's eyes. He'd got to know him quite well.

'Mike,' said Finlay at the end, 'how'd you get into this?'

'It's a long story, Jerry. But like the captain said, we don't 'ave time to talk now.'

'Ten bars of gold? That's what you want us to say?'

'That's right. And all the rest.'

The three men went to the communications room, situated in a curtained-off area beside the bridge. By now it was eight p.m. There was no contact planned and no other officer in the communications area.

Mike watched in silence. The captain scribbled out a message and passed it to Finlay, who made a few pencilled changes and handed it to Mike. It read:

'URGENT. Deck supervisor Michael Cox advises hijack attempt imminent with death of all on board a probability. He is part of scheme, but ready to reveal details in exchange for ten bars of gold, flight to Zurich from Murmansk and new passport under new name. Remind that we have on board already two hundred and fifty-seven bars gold. Suggest we comply a.s.a.p. on understanding that if no details forthcoming Cox charged with attempted piracy. Meanwhile suggest contact both MoD and Soviet authorities to get joint agreement and begin preparation of suitable response. Cox also has own ideas about suitable response. Message ends.'

Coding the message took time. Each letter had to be matched to a number in a pre-designated page in a random-number book, only two copies of which existed – one in Finlay's hand at the moment, the other in Ocean Pioneers' HQ in Aberdeen. Transmission, too, was a slow business – the list of numbers had to be read out one by one, and copied down by whoever was on duty at the other end. Whoever it was knew by the length and complexity of the message that it was not standard information. Even before it was over, someone would be on the phone to his colleagues, and to the Ministry of Defence in London.

There was a pause of ten minutes, the radio equivalent of stunned silence.

Then, in clear, came two words: 'Please repeat.' Finlay repeated the string of numbers and ended by saying, in clear: 'Confirming, confirming.'

Kohlmeyer ordered coffee. The time began to stretch out.

Fifteen minutes.

Twenty minutes.

Half an hour.

An hour.

Then came a voice reading back a string of numbers. Finlay scribbled them down and then laboriously translated:

'Sorry delay. This is Sunday evening. London and Moscow give outline approval. Insist agreement must depend details from Cox leading to successful foiling of plot and landing of gold. Any failure renders agreement null. Urgently await your response. Message ends.'

Mike nodded and began to talk.

He told Kohlmeyer about his own scheme, his involvement with Krassnik, the American's Middle East contacts, the arrangement with the single rose, his own theory about the nature of the hijack, and his contact with the SBS.

Finlay said: 'So let's get one thing clear – you don't really know, do you?'

'Know what?'

'That there's a sub down there?'

'I know there's a hijack planned. You can guess the rest as well as I can.'

'Guess. We can't deal in guesses.'

'Yes, you can. You 'ave to. Then maybe the people in London can find something to confirm them.'

None of the men had noticed during the negotiations that for perhaps half an hour now the *Stephaniturm* had begun to roll. Kohlmeyer glanced out of the porthole. 'The weather is not looking so good,' he said. 'Perhaps we have not so much time.'

The message from the *Stephaniturm* had been telephoned from Aberdeen to a private number in London, at the home of a man we shall call Sir Anthony Grey, who reported to the Foreign Minister and was known in the corridors of the Ministry of Defence and Century House (the headquarters of MI6), and would even have been recognized at the barracks of the SAS in Bradbury Lines, Herefordshire.

Why such things had to happen on Sunday evenings was beyond him – presumably in accordance with the same natural laws that compelled toast to fall buttered side downwards. It had taken him two hours to gather together the five men he needed to form his 'crisis committee' and all five, haggard and resigned, were gathered around a large rosewood table in a Whitehall office. On the table were telephones, paper, maps and a litter of polystyrene cups. It was approaching midnight. All five men had been dragged from comfortable evenings with families or friends, or – in the case of the Russian – a mistress. Each knew they had a working night and probably the whole of the next day ahead of them.

They were a diverse bunch – Sir Anthony from the Foreign Office, two senior representatives from the MoD, two men from the higher ranks of the two Intelligence services, MI5 and MI6, and a lugubrious first secretary from the Russian Embassy. The two MoD men knew each other, as did the two Intelligence representatives. But the Foreign Office, MoD and Intelligence men all harboured suspicions towards each other, and all five regarded the Russian, Igor Tschernik, with distaste.

Tschernik was tired, frustrated and unhappy. He'd been told by Sir Anthony that the Intelligence men were from the Foreign Office, but he knew better. He had known nothing of the gold, let alone the hijack attempt, until an hour ago, and had only a few minutes' briefing from his ambassador to go on. He could make no decisions himself, and was in effect the go-between for Whitehall, the embassy and Moscow.

'Gentlemen,' Sir Anthony was saying, 'you've seen the latest message. I suggest that the sooner we know what's in that flat in Albemarle Street the better. I suppose, Mr Tschernik, you know nothing of this?'

The Russian looked up glumly. He said nothing, but closed his eyes in suffering ignorance and shook his head.

'I think the police can offer the most discreet approach,' Sir Anthony said, raising an eyebrow at his MoD colleague, who nodded. Sir Anthony reached for the telephone, called Scotland Yard, explained about the address and asked for an urgent response 'in the national interest'. He did not say why he made the request.

'What of this man Krassnik, John?' he then asked.

'Do we really want the Americans in on all this?'

'No. At least, not at this stage. Perhaps a general query to Langley might raise something. Can you handle?'

Tschernik broke in: 'Sir Anthony, I'm instructed by my ambassador to ask how a criminal came to be aboard the' – he glanced down at some notes in front of him – 'the *Stephaniturm*.'

'Mr Tschernik.' Sir Anthony Grey was in no mood to accept any implied criticism. 'The *Stephaniturm* is a German vessel contracted to an English company contracted to *both* our governments. There was an official decision to play down security. Any fault – and I do not believe there is any – is borne equally by both governments.'

'We shall see.'

'No doubt, Mr Tschernik, no doubt. But I must remind you that any investigation will only intensify the embarrassment. Our task at present is to work together to solve the problem, not allot blame.'

They began to talk about the possible identity of the hijackers, assuming they actually existed. At this stage a number of Britons and Russians in London and Moscow had a strong suspicion that the other partner was somehow implicated. But there were numerous other possibilities to be considered – the IRA, the Red Brigades, the Palestinians, some group of freelance pirates. All seemed equally unlikely.

The two calls came through within minutes of each other. The CIA in Langley, Virginia, reported that Krassnik was a known arms dealer, a middleman who supplied any number of Middle Eastern groups and countries. He had never worked overtly against American interests. Various of his Eastern bloc contacts were questionable, but he had brought so much cash to US arms firms that no one had seen fit to clamp down on him. Besides, he had friends in high places.

The police commissioner who telephoned informed Sir Anthony that the flat in Albemarle Street was empty, totally empty, stripped bare, except for the telephone, on which there was no number, some cellophane wrapping and a withered red rose. The telephone company had been bullied by Scotland Yard into tracing the line, checking the number and finding the order form which had been signed several months previously by a Mr Habib Hassani. By the early hours of Monday morning the Home Office computer had provided the information that a Habib Hassani had entered the country two months earlier as a tourist. He was a Libyan.

Other calls were made to the head of the Institute of Strategic Studies, to the SAS in Herefordshire, to the Russian Embassy, to the MoD and to the West German police computer centre in Wiesbaden, the world's best source of information on international terrorism. Scenarios emerged, were discussed, then vanished.

Early breakfast arrived. That Monday a number of offices around London were occupied unusually early. Information began to flow into the Whitehall office.

By nine o'clock the bleary-eyed team had begun to see the problem for what it was. According to Wiesbaden, Hassani was one of several pseudonyms used by Major Abdel Moneim el Huni, one of the two members of Libya's Revolutionary Command

Council who were responsible both for the five thousand non-Libyan terrorists training in Libya and for Libyan terrorists abroad. Libya had enough sophisticated hardware to stage a hijack almost anywhere on earth; but an airborne approach demanded a base, which on NATO's northern flank would have been easily detected. She also had ships and submarines.

A number of possibilities were checked.

By a process of elimination, the most likely hypothesis was that the hijack would be carried out by a Libyan submarine. Checks were run. Enquiries, via NATO computers, revealed two unidentified traces: one recorded in Gibraltar soon after the *Stephaniturm*'s departure, another on file in the US base outside Reykjavik. They could have been made by the same submarine, which could now be in the vicinity of the *Stephaniturm*.

'So,' Sir Anthony summarized, 'the next problem that faces us is to find out where this hypothetical submarine is.'

'I think I know,' said the MI6 man. 'The *Edinburgh* has been pretty useful strategically. She's just over six hundred feet long, almost exactly the same length as a nuclear sub. We've made use of that factor on several occasions, because a submarine can sit alongside in the wreck's sonar shadow. Both sides do it' – he glanced at Tschernik – 'and now the Libyans have got in on the act. Except they obviously haven't chosen the *Edinburgh*. If they're anywhere, they're down by the *Hermann Schoemann.*'

It took another half an hour to sketch a likely scenario for the assault. Clearly it wouldn't be a matter of a sudden torpedo attack. The *Stephaniturm* would have to be approached and boarded if the gold was to be taken off safely. Only then would the crew be killed and the vessel sunk.

'But there'll be plenty of time for the ship to call for help,' said one of the MoD men.

'Time enough to call for it,' Sir Anthony responded. 'Not enough time for it to come. Am I right, James?'

'Right, Tony.'

Both men knew of Cox's plans, of course. Both knew, without even discussing the matter, that the response would represent a high-level risk. The trouble with these operations was that they had to work. Of course, the PM would be informed before the event, and it wouldn't go ahead without her approval, but both knew the rules in the event of failure. The interview would be only the beginning. Their heads would roll. Others would follow. An inquiry. Press criticism. Goodbye to politics.

Better, perhaps, if direct responsibility could be avoided.

Sometime around midday Sir Anthony turned tired eyes to Tschernik and said: 'We are agreed on the most likely nature of the opposition. Time to devise a response. I suggest, Mr Tschernik, since your country is so close, that you assume responsibility.'

'How?'

'Mr Tschernik, really, do you need us to tell you how to deploy your forces? You have nuclear submarines, aeroplanes, ships. Please make appropriate arrangements.'

Tschernik asked for time. He went out to call the embassy in Kensington Palace Gardens, returning after ten long minutes.

'Sir Anthony, we have no submarines nearby. The weather is becoming worse. It will take twenty-four hours or more to get ships to the area. We suggest that since it is well known that NATO maintains permanent watch on our northern flanks, you should arrange the necessary protection.'

Sir Anthony put a thumb and forefinger to his eyelids. The games these people played.

'We must consider our options, Mr Tschernik. Will you be good enough . . . ?' Tschernik was already rising. 'You'll find a waiting room opposite.'

When he was gone, Sir Anthony placed a call to Aberdeen. As Tschernik said, the weather north of Murmansk was deteriorating. The *Stephaniturm* reported that the divers were exhausted, and it would soon no longer be practical to continue with the operation.

Time was running out.

Sir Anthony addressed the MI6 man: 'James?'

'We know they have nuclear subs working out

of Murmansk. They know we know. We have subs up there. They know. We know they know. We monitor each other all the time. But neither of us is going to admit it, even if it means losing the gold.'

'Mm. Let's be clear about this. We stand to get £8 million, give or take a bit. The Russians stand to get sixteen million. And yet you're saying . . .'

'Frankly, it's not worth the candle. Neither side is going to negotiate a change of grand strategic policy, certainly not in the time available, on the off-chance of gaining pocket money.'

Sir Anthony knew enough of the machiavellian politics of his colleague to know that he was serious.

'So we just leave things to run their course?'

The MI6 man nodded.

'I understand. But a bit harsh, James, all the same. And, if I may say so, a bit narrow-minded. I think the PM would back me on this one. True, the gold alone may not be all that important. But if this chap Cox is right, and the ship gets blown sky-high, the political cost would be unacceptable. Damn it, there are journalists on board.'

'Doomed journalists.'

There was a brief silence while each of them contemplated the political consequences of inaction. Inaction was merely failure by another name. Action, then, was necessary, even inevitable. Better look on the bright side, and contemplate the consequences of success.

Sir Anthony, who had long believed he should be ambassador in Washington, felt the mood, and summed it up with a decision. 'It's too risky. We have to do something.' He turned to one of the MoD men. 'George?'

'We could have a sub there in a few hours.'

'What's a few?'

'Twelve. Give or take.'

'Too slow.'

There was a long silence, marked by the slow tick of a wall clock. Options were running out. 'Well,' said Sir Anthony, raising the thought that was in all minds. 'This chap Cox seems to be ahead of us on several counts.'

The MI6 man picked up the hint. 'No point having a unit trained for this sort of op and not using it. I'm sure the PM will back you.'

'Us, James, us.'

'Of course. Shall I make the call?'

'Please do.'

On the *Stephaniturm*, the conditions had gone from bad to worse. The gale had increased to Force Eleven. The ship swung and tossed in mountainous seas. Few people slept. Diving halted. The *Stephaniturm* hove to. The divers were utterly exhausted. There were a number of minor injuries, and an increase in ear infections. Only the success of the operation so far sustained morale – three hundred and eighty-six ingots raised – £40 million worth – with seventy-nine still to go. Privately, the diving supervisor had advised Kohlmeyer that there could be no more diving. Even seventy-nine bars – with a value of nearly £8 million – were not worth going for if that meant endangering lives, especially when the project had already been over eighty per cent successful. The two agreed that as soon as the storm abated the *Stephaniturm* would make for Murmansk.

The two-day pause, 5 and 6 October, was welcomed by both Russia and Britain. For one thing, in that screaming, icy wind, not even the Libyans would be foolhardy enough to risk an assault. They, too, would have to wait for the gale to die.

Towards the end of 5 October the ship received a radio message, which was decoded by Finlay and handed to Kohlmeyer – the only two men other than Mike who were aware of the true situation. It read:

'Advise the probable hijacker is Libyan sub at present hove to in sonar shadow of *Hermann Schoemann*. No knowledge of plans, but clearly departure from site is last possible moment for attack. Suggest delay as long as possible. British response underway along lines proposed by Cox. Also advise events now covered by Official Secrets Act and D notice.'

Early on 6 October the wind dropped again.

Kohlmeyer was forced to widen the circle of those who knew of the possible hijack. He needed time, and in order to win it he had to fix the *Stephaniturm* over the *Edinburgh* as long as possible. He called in the diving supervisor and explained matters, allowing him only three minutes of incredulous questions.

'We have to dive,' he said, 'or explain why we are staying here. Can the divers make it again?'

'I don't know. Those guys need fresh air. They've got ten days of decompression ahead of them. We've already established a record for diving at depth in suits. And these conditions are hell. By rights, they should all be dead on their feet with exhaustion. OK, I shouldn't do it, but I'll challenge them to go down for one more shift.'

Which is exactly what happened. By midday on Wednesday 7 October, the *Stephaniturm* had on board four hundred and forty-one ingots, with only a further twenty-four left on the seabed. That afternoon the diving supervisor reported back to Kohlmeyer.

'That's it. No more diving,' he told him.

'Which means,' Kohlmeyer said to Finlay, 'we have to go. We can't sit here doing nothing.'

He sent a message to Aberdeen asking for guidance.

The reply came: 'Sit tight. Await help.'

All four men – Kohlmeyer, Finlay, Mike and the diving supervisor – read this reply together, hunched over the table in the communications room. Mike had completed another shift. Strangely, though he was the direct cause of the present predicament, he was still an accepted member of the community. In the knowledge they shared, in their common danger, they were as one, and any feelings of bitterness towards him were, in the present crisis, suppressed.

'For God's sake,' Finlay said. 'We're not even sure yet that there *is* a sub down there. And if there is, we don't know whether there is anybody to rescue us or not.'

Kohlmeyer shrugged. 'We have no choice. If we stay here, they will see we have stopped diving. We shall be a standing duck.'

'Sitting,' muttered Finlay.

'Standing, sitting, duck, bird, chicken. What's the difference? We have to go. Are the divers up? The bell is locked on?'

'Yes, they're all resting. I'll tell them to start decompressing. They'll be relieved.'

'They're lucky,' Kohlmeyer said with a wan smile. 'They get less pressure, we get more, eh?'

The captain went through to the bridge, Finlay remained in communications and the diving supervisor went below. Kohlmeyer spoke into the ship's intercom: 'We have good news. We have the gold, or almost all of it. No more diving. We go home now!'

At once he ordered full steam ahead, due south.

Full speed, thought Mike; she's not meant for speed. Ten knots cruising speed, twelve knots flat out. What was that against a sub that could touch twenty-five knots? If they had their wits about them they'd be up in five minutes and alongside in another five. Good God, that might even allow them enough time to get away with it.

He went out on deck and looked back over the stern, past the A-frame beside which he had spent so many hours. He leant against the gas storage cylinders, most of them used up now that the diving was almost finished.

For ten minutes the *Stephaniturm* ploughed southwards. Below decks diving support personnel who had been tense and exhausted for lack of sleep for a month opened some of the few bottles of wine that had been brought on board for just such an occasion. In the decompression chambers divers slept, drank fruit juice or ate, or chatted to friends on the intercom. In the wheelhouse Kohlmeyer prayed there would be no hijack, that Mike was crazy, that there would be no need for a response from anyone.

He was, of course, disappointed. Just twelve minutes after the *Stephaniturm* left the site of the *Edinburgh* a dark-grey shape rose through the icy swell half a mile to the east and a fraction to the north. For perhaps ten seconds no one saw her. Mike was looking aft, Kohlmeyer forward. It was someone on the mess deck, sipping a Coke and staring out through a porthole, who spotted her first. 'Jesus Christ!' he shouted. 'What the fuck's that?'

Everyone in the mess crowded to a porthole and then stumbled out into the chill wind on deck.

Simultaneously a call up to the bridge informed Kohlmeyer, who veered off to starboard.

On deck Mike gripped the rails, stood watching with the others and said nothing. There were half a dozen, a dozen, a score of men with him, each shouting his own comment or replying to another.

'A bloody sub!'

'What's she up to?'

'Anyone see any markings?'

'Nah!' This from someone with binoculars. 'Not a dicky-bird.'

'Is she heading our way?'

'She's fucking closing on us!'

'Who the hell are they?'

'Cutting us off!'

'I know that silhouette! That's an old American sub! Haven't seen one of those since Korea!'

Steadily, the evil grey shape closed on the *Stephaniturm* until she was running abreast less than a quarter of a mile away.

Kohlmeyer was shouting into his radio: 'There it is! *Um Gottes Willen!* Right beside us, distance three hundred, four hundred metres. Bearing ninety degrees. Now there are men on deck . . . they're loading the gun . . .'

On the *Stephaniturm*'s stern, thirty men watched,

stunned into silence by the sight of three figures bringing the four-inch gun on the submarine's bows to bear on the ship.

There was a puff of smoke, followed in a sequence of microseconds by a dull boom and a splash a hundred yards to starboard. The trajectory had been low. The shot had clearly been intended for the wheelhouse. It must have passed only a few feet over the top. The silence on deck was broken by a stream of shouts.

'Blow us apart!'

'What the hell is . . . ?'

'Bloody Russkies, trying to take all the gold!'

'Russkies on a Yankee sub? Get away!'

'Look out! She's having another go!'

Kohlmeyer radioed from the wheelhouse: 'What are you people doing? Where is this protection? Two hundred metres! She can't miss!' It seemed to him he was staring straight down the barrel of a gun.

'Full astern!' he yelled, and threw a lever. At once the two Deutz twenty-four-hundred-horsepower diesel engines died, to pick up again in a shuddering reverse thrust. On the stern the crowd of men tottered forward, grabbing at each other and the railings to counteract the change of direction.

At that moment the submarine's gun fired again. The shell had been perfectly aimed. But in the instant of firing, the *Stephaniturm*'s propellers had begun to slow her. The shell, which would have driven straight into the wheelhouse, killing Kohlmeyer outright and removing the radio, passed immediately in front of the wheelhouse's windows. It actually clipped the top of the line of railing that ran round the bridge deck.

On the submarine the three-man gun crew stared in amazement at the plume of spray that leapt up a hundred yards beyond the *Stephaniturm*. It must have seemed to them that the shell had passed clean through the bridge.

Ten seconds went by. The *Stephaniturm* began to drop astern of the submarine, which suddenly switched direction, heeling to port as it swung to starboard. The gun crew staggered, righted themselves and attempted to realign the gun, but for several seconds were unable to counteract the port list.

'That was too close!' Kohlmeyer bawled into his radio. 'We should all be dead! One hundred and fifty metres and closing! I thought you said you sent help!'

Meanwhile Mike had edged his way round the deck, along with a dozen others, to stand at the bow rails, staring at the submarine as it slowed in the path of the *Stephaniturm*, her propellers clawing her to a standstill.

'This is it!' he said. 'This is bloody it!'

He saw the barrel of the four-inch gun swing round again. The range was no more than eighty yards. It'd be like hitting a barn door with a twelve-bore. The *Stephaniturm* was, in Kohlmeyer's words, a standing bird.

* * *

But the gun did not fire, for at that moment, above the gusting wind and beat of the engines, another sound broke through. Mike's attention had been so riveted on the submarine that he had not seen what would otherwise have been as obvious as a punch in the eye – a Hercules transporter sweeping in over the waves at no more than two hundred and fifty feet. After its fifteen-hundred-mile, four-hour flight from Gosport, it had zeroed in on the *Stephaniturm*'s coordinates and was heading straight for the submarine.

The gunners looked up, registered, swung the gun, paused, glanced towards a gesticulating figure in the conning tower, then abandoned the gun for the safety of the hatch.

They were already too late. Within ten seconds the plane was almost overhead. From the open ramp at the rear of its cavernous hold came a stream of objects. Two writhing black shapes that resolved themselves into automatically inflating dinghies, and a dozen men in winterized frogmen's suits, holding weapons, cords streaming from packs that contained paragliding chutes.

With little smacking noises audible above the noise of the receding plane, the chutes opened. Even before the first of the gunners on the deck of the sub had vanished into the interior, even as the sub herself began to sink back beneath the waves, the first of the paragliders was closing on the sub, weaving and bobbing in the stiff breeze. The first man hit the foredeck near the gun too hard, slid on the slick metal and vanished down the far side. The second and third men were on target, some twenty feet behind the conning tower, landing lightly with a neat pull on their drawstrings, releasing their chutes and dropping on to their knees on the rolling deck.

By now the hatch was closed, the water foaming over the bows. The one remaining gunner, about to be sacrificed in the crash-dive, hammered briefly against the metal, then turned, hands raised, as the two men ran towards him, waving him aside with their weapons. What they could do to stop a submarine submerging, Mike could not imagine. Several others drifted down on to the sub, and a further four guided themselves towards the dinghies, now inflated and riding the icy, white-tipped swell. As they hauled themselves aboard and whipped the engines into life, the two leading men on the sub slapped what looked like limpet mines against the conning tower, while the abandoned gunner looked on aghast.

With a quick gesture to their mates, the two leapt clear, followed instantly by the others and the sub's crewman. Dressed in heavy woollen clothing under waterproofs, he would have sunk in seconds if one of the dinghies had not been there to fish him out.

The sub, its conning tower slicing through the

rising water, sank fast, leaving the SBS team gathering themselves in the two dinghies.

For a moment the crowd at the railings of the *Stephaniturm* watched spellbound, waiting for whatever might happen next. Clearly something was expected, for the dinghies were bouncing along in the wake of the submarine, shadowing it as it vanished from sight. As if responding to the unstated wishes of her crew, the *Stephaniturm* began to move, keeping Mike and the others close to the action.

Suddenly, perhaps a hundred yards from where it vanished, a gout of water exploded upwards with a dull boom.

Another blast.

Then, still driving forward under full power, the sub began to re-emerge from the depths. It was very much changed. The conning tower had practically vanished, leaving nothing but a jagged ruin of metal. The mines had blown a six-foot hole in the top of the sub, allowing water to pour in. Below the tower there would have been another set of watertight manholes, but the blast must have loosened them. The inside must have been reduced to a panic-stricken chaos of darkness, gushing water and screams. Knowing at once that to stay down would be suicidal, the captain had blown the tanks to bring her back up, perhaps hoping to outrun his pursuers on the surface.

No chance. The dinghies buzzed and bounced alongside the great grey shape, like wolves attacking the flanks of a mammoth.

Again she was boarded. Now, though, the men had access to the interior. Two men vanished into the shattered conning tower, emerging within seconds.

Again the quick gesture, the rapid retreat.

And again two blasts in rapid succession.

This time she was mortally wounded. The engines died and an oil slick, like black arterial blood, spread out from her rear end. Wallowing in the swell, she drifted to a halt, the swell surging up her flanks.

Within half a minute the *Stephaniturm* was twenty yards away, where she reversed thrust in response to a wave from the SBS commander.

From that position Mike had a fine view of the end of the drama. The SBS closing in, some re-boarding, arms levelled, waiting for the surrender. The appearance of the first of the crew members, hands raised. The slow, resentful emergence of the rest of the crew, fifteen men in all. Finally, the four back-and-forth journeys to the *Stephaniturm*, as the SBS men and the sub's crew came aboard, in silence, to vanish below.

Once the SBS commander had checked the sub over and contacted London, it became clear that she would be no use to anyone. She was already forty years old, and outmoded in every respect. The cost of arranging to tow her back to England would be exorbitant, and the Russians certainly had no interest in salvaging her.

So she was scuttled, by two SBS men, with a hiss

of escaping air and a flurry of water. As the two men pulled clear, she sank silently, dropping down to the seabed eight hundred feet below, another corpse in a graveyard of ships.

Only then, when the SBS started asking questions, did answers emerge. For their ears only, though. There was a lot they wanted to know, a lot to pass on to London, with as little as possible divulged to Mike. The only thing he learnt, as everyone else did, was the nationality of the hijackers.

So how did Gaddafi get to hear of this? The question ricocheted back and forth between Mike's colleagues, who would rapidly have become ex-colleagues if they had known the answer to their question. What bastard had put our income, our chance at wealth, our *lives* at risk? Mike prayed no one discovered the truth before he was out of there.

An hour later Kohlmeyer, Finlay and Mike sat in the captain's office staring at a message Finlay had decoded five minutes previously. It read:

'MoD advise information blackout in national and international interests. HMG in full agreement with Soviet Union. Please inform Soviet delegates on board. Propose suitable explanation for majority of crew. Arrange suitable cover for disappearance of gold to be paid to Cox. Reply soonest.'

'Well,' said Finlay, 'seems like they want us to do all the work. We have until tomorrow to wrap things up. But, Werner, that's too far off. If we don't take action soon, there'll be a riot. The place is wild with rumour. Everyone wants to use the radio. The Russians are going spare . . .'

Kohlmeyer raised a hand. 'I know. We have to explain things at once to the Russian and British officials. Between us, we must solve this problem of the gold for Cox.'

'Ah, yes, the ten bars,' said Finlay, with heavy sarcasm. 'The most important thing of all, that. You really seem to have come out of this OK, Mike. You should give lessons.'

'Now don't start nothing,' said Mike harshly. 'You owe me. Let alone I just saved your lives, you wouldn't be 'ere, wouldn't 'ave no gold at all if it wasn't for me.'

'How do you make that out?'

'It was only me threatening to mount a pirate operation what forced them into giving you a contract.'

Finlay huffed through his nose in disdain.

'Gentlemen,' Kohlmeyer cut in, 'there is no time to argue. What of this gold?'

'I've got a suggestion,' Mike asked.

'Thought you might have,' Finlay muttered.

'It's easy enough, but I want to put it to all concerned. So perhaps we could get them in here now and put them out of their misery.'

Kohlmeyer nodded, pressed his intercom button and broadcast a call for a conference to include the Russians and the MoD representatives. Within a few minutes they had all crowded into the cabin and found seats, the Russians as grim as statues, the British angry and puzzled.

Kohlmeyer himself brought them up to date with the facts as he knew them.

The Russians asked to use the radio to contact Moscow, which could be done via Murmansk. Some acrimonious talk with the military authorities there eventually provided a link, and Moscow confirmed Kohlmeyer's information.

When the conference reconvened, Kohlmeyer said: 'Our first problem is to control the curiosity of those on board. I suggest that we should tell the truth. Only if we have absolute trust from those on board can we expect their cooperation. Do you agree?'

'Hadn't we better consider leaving the whole thing a mystery?' said one of the British officials.

'Mr Finlay and I have talked about that. It won't do. Clearly there have been many security leaks. The Libyans knew about us. The Russians know about the Libyans. I do not believe that we can ask for total discretion when others have already been indiscreet.'

Mike coughed. 'Then there's the gold,' he said. All eyes turned to him.

'OK, Mike, let's hear it.'

Mike had prepared his speech to seem unrepentant, assertive.

'First, I must remind you of the agreement made with me by the British government. My life will be worth nothing if I do not disappear. I'll have the Libyans after me and the guy who set the whole thing up. I need enough cash to last the rest of my life. That's why I want the gold.

'Secondly, I haven't been greedy. I have been planning on getting the gold for years. I could have taken the whole lot on my own. You're bloody lucky I didn't. And I might have asked for a whole lot more. Your lives – *our* lives – are worth more than a million quid. Now the problem is how to hand over ten bars of gold to me and then somehow account for their disappearance. So first off, how many bars are left down there?'

'Twenty-four. That's all.'

'OK. It's simple. You all, we all, agree there weren't twenty-four but thirty-four bars left down there. Just add in my ten to the bars the divers didn't fetch up. Delete the last ten numbers from your manifest. 'Oo's to know? No one's announced the actual numbers of bars recovered to the media yet. The journalists are blocked by D notices. That means they can only publish anything at all with the government's agreement. Right?'

He raised his eyebrows to an MoD man, who nodded.

'OK. Then all you need to do is tell the truth to everyone else. The whole bloody lot already know exactly 'ow much was brought up. Everyone saw the sub. Whatever you tell them about me, you can also tell them that they owe their lives to me. You can also point out that no one's going to lose out much. What's ten bars out of four 'undred and forty-one? Two per cent? Not much. I'd say you'd all got a bargain.'

The Russians were already in a huddle.

'Outright deception. Forger,' said Finlay.

'The whole thing's a deception – but only of the public,' said Mike. 'Nothing new in that. No one on board is deceived. You've got official orders to organize a cover-up. This is 'ow you do it. Seems to me that if you've got to be dishonest, this is the most honest way of doing it. Anyway, if any of you can think of a better way, go ahead.'

It took ten minutes of discussion for all those involved to realize that there was no better way. The alternative to losing the gold was to lose Mike, and he had long ago ensured that there were too many in the know for that to be possible. There followed another hour of radio time to confirm the arrangements with London and Moscow.

It was already after ten p.m. Kohlmeyer was exhausted, and would need sleep before the docking in Murmansk the following day, but he insisted on making the long public explanation necessary to keep the peace on board ship.

16

The *Stephaniturm* approached the Kola Inlet early on the morning of the eighth. Mike took a call from Kohlmeyer, asking him to remain in his cabin. He was joined five minutes later by one of the Russians, who told him London and Moscow had agreed that he was to be given 'special treatment'.

Not that he would have seen much if he had been on deck. The hills of Polyarnyo and Vaenga were the same. But the bases themselves were invisible – under instructions from Murmansk, the *Stephaniturm* kept well to the centre of the approaches.

Through his porthole Mike could see that Murmansk itself had changed a good deal. The railhead was larger. The cranes were like those of any dockyard in the world. He glimpsed a delegation of stolid, formally clad officials waiting on the quayside. He read afterwards of the wary smiles, the formal congratulations in stilted English, the long discussions in Kohlmeyer's cabin, but he played no part in these events.

First, there was the gold to be unshipped. Then the Russians and British together supervised the formal counting of the gold bars, all four hundred and forty-one. Ten of these were counted off and set separately on the hoist that would lift the gold on to the deck. Of the remaining four hundred and thirty-one ingots, the Russians counted out their share – two-thirds of fifty-five per cent: a hundred and fifty-eight bars. The division was not exact and had to be balanced by a currency transaction later. All the bars, Mike's included, were then lifted to the deck by the *Stephaniturm*'s hoist and from the deck transferred to a cargo hoist. Ashore, a Soviet insurance official signed the receipt.

During all this time Mike remained in his cabin with his Russian companion, missing, as well as the reception on the quayside, the champagne and vodka celebrations that surrounded the crew and diving personnel in Murmansk's best hotel.

He was escorted ashore only late in the afternoon. No one saw him leave. It was already twilight. A chill wind, foreshadowing winter, sliced its way around the cranes and wagons lining the docks. He shivered in his overcoat. Ashore, he was escorted for five minutes up the quayside – past the spot where he had once seen a gaunt skeleton of a man with a hole through his head – to a huge and desolate warehouse. At the entrance was parked a grey army truck. His companion slid back one of the fifteen-foot-high corrugated-iron doors. Just inside stood a single pallet and on it lay his ten bars of gold.

Two soldiers stood guard. The Russian official produced from his breast pocket a piece of paper.

'Count and sign,' he said.

Mike looked closely at the ten bars. One, he was pleased to note, was the bar he had always considered his own private property, the one that had begun his whole involvement with the gold: KP 1926. He nodded, reached for the paper, signed and pocketed the carbon. That would be important – it was his proof of ownership.

'When do we go?'

'Now. No one want you here,' said the official.

The Russian waved an arm, and the two soldiers rolled the pallet with its golden burden across the concrete floor to the warehouse entrance. They clattered across a railway line to the truck. One climbed up and threw back the canvas cover. The other began to pass up the gold bars.

'You have passport?' said Ivan.

Mike felt in his inside pocket and nodded.

'For Switzerland you need no visa, yes?'

'No.'

That was a relief. Switzerland it was. Popular he might not be, but at least they were going to fulfil their side of the bargain.

One soldier remained in the back of the truck. Mike was waved into the passenger seat. His guardian climbed up beside him. The other soldier hauled himself into the driver's seat and swung the truck around to steer an erratic, bumpy course down the quayside, avoiding potholes and crates of cargo. Of the rest of the *Stephaniturm*'s crew there was no sign.

Murmansk still seemed a dump. Grey. Little traffic. A steam locomotive shrieked mournfully beyond the warehouses. Back from the dock lay a line of barracks. Four soldiers marched out of a glowing doorway. The town's buildings were drab, concrete blocks. Perhaps a few were survivors of German bombs.

Ten minutes later the truck bumped towards a bleak airfield, guarded by barbed wire and, at the entrance, a couple of concrete offices. It slowed briefly to allow the barrier to open, then accelerated through and swung around the perimeter of the airfield, a further half a mile to a collection of hangars and dimly lit office blocks. On the runway beyond the buildings an Aeroflot Ilyushin stood in the gathering gloom. The truck pulled up beside the steps. A large black limousine was parked a hundred yards away. Mike could not see if there was anyone in it. There was no one in sight.

'Is this for me?'

'*All* for you, Mr Cox.'

'Good grief. It must seat a hundred.'

'One hundred and thirty.'

'Where's the gold going?'

'Please?'

'What'll you do with the gold?'

'Gold is cargo. In cargo space.'

'No. Put it in with me.'

The Russian paused, then said: 'Is OK.'

The two soldiers unloaded the ten bars on to the tarmac, and then, as instructed, began to carry it two bars at a time up the steps. Mike picked up KP 1926 himself and walked up the steps, the bar on one arm, his case held in the other hand. In the empty plane he seated himself behind a wing. The gold was stacked on seats beside him, three bars to a seat.

Finally the Russian asked for his passport.

Mike handed it over. The man pulled a stamp and ink pad from his pocket, and carefully gave him a visa and exit stamp.

'Good journey,' he said.

'Ta, Ivan.'

The Russian left. The two soldiers pulled back the steps. The door swung closed. A voice came through the loudspeaker system: 'Seat-belt, please.'

The engines began to whine. The plane swung round until it was pointing due north, away from the buildings. The brakes came off and the plane accelerated down the runway. It climbed over Murmansk itself, the dark shadows of the concrete apartment blocks now punctuated by lights, and banked over the harbour.

Mike looked down. He could just make out the *Stephaniturm* lying at her berth, carefully isolated from the other cargo vessels. The harbour drifted out of sight beneath the wing. Ahead the water spread northwards past Vaenga and Polyarnyo to the icy wastes of the Arctic.

The plane banked in a hundred-and-eighty-degree turn, revealed a final glimpse of Murmansk under the port wing and headed south.

OTHER TITLES IN SERIES FROM 22 BOOKS

Available now at newsagents and booksellers
or use the order form provided

SOLDIER A SAS:	Behind Iraqi Lines
SOLDIER B SAS:	Heroes of the South Atlantic
SOLDIER C SAS:	Secret War in Arabia
SOLDIER D SAS:	The Colombian Cocaine War
SOLDIER E SAS:	Sniper Fire in Belfast
SOLDIER F SAS:	Guerrillas in the Jungle
SOLDIER G SAS:	The Desert Raiders
SOLDIER H SAS:	The Headhunters of Borneo
SOLDIER I SAS:	Eighteen Years in the Elite Force
SOLDIER J SAS:	Counter-insurgency in Aden
SOLDIER K SAS:	Mission to Argentina
SOLDIER L SAS:	The Embassy Siege
SOLDIER M SAS:	Invisible Enemy in Kazakhstan
SOLDIER N SAS:	The Gambian Bluff
SOLDIER O SAS:	The Bosnian Inferno
SOLDIER P SAS:	Night Fighters in France
SOLDIER Q SAS:	Kidnap the Emperor!
SOLDIER R SAS:	Death on Gibraltar
SOLDIER S SAS:	The Samarkand Hijack
SOLDIER T SAS:	War on the Streets
SOLDIER U SAS:	Bandit Country
SOLDIER V SAS:	Into Vietnam
SOLDIER W SAS:	Guatemala – Journey into Evil
SOLDIER X SAS:	Operation Takeaway
SOLDIER Y SAS:	Days of the Dead
SOLDIER Z SAS:	For King and Country

continued overleaf . . .

SOLDIER OF FORTUNE 1: Valin's Raiders
SOLDIER OF FORTUNE 2: The Korean Contract
SOLDIER OF FORTUNE 3: The Vatican Assignment
SOLDIER OF FORTUNE 4: Operation Nicaragua
SOLDIER OF FORTUNE 5: Action in the Arctic
SOLDIER OF FORTUNE 6: The Khmer Hit
SOLDIER OF FORTUNE 7: Blue on Blue
SOLDIER OF FORTUNE 8: Target the Death-dealer
SOLDIER OF FORTUNE 9: The Berlin Alternative
MERCENARY 10: The Blue-eyed Boy
MERCENARY 11: Oliver's Army
MERCENARY 12: The Corsican Crisis
MERCENARY 13: Gunners' Moon

* * *

MARINE A SBS: Terrorism on the North Sea
MARINE B SBS: The Aegean Campaign
MARINE C SBS: The Florida Run
MARINE D SBS: Windswept
MARINE E SBS: The Hong Kong Gambit
MARINE F SBS: Royal Target
MARINE G SBS: China Seas
MARINE H SBS: The Burma Offensive
MARINE I SBS: Escape from Azerbaijan
MARINE J SBS: The East African Mission

* * *

WINGS 1: Typhoon Strike
WINGS 2: The MiG Lover
WINGS 3: The Invisible Warrior
WINGS 4: Ferret Flight
WINGS 5: Norwegian Fire
WINGS 6: Behind the Lines

All at £4.99

All 22 Books are available at your bookshop, or can be ordered from:

22 Books
Mail Order Department
Little, Brown and Company
Brettenham House
Lancaster Place
London WC2E 7EN

Alternatively, you may fax your order to the above address. Fax number: 0171 911 8100.

Payments can be made by cheque or postal order, payable to Little, Brown and Company (UK), or by credit card (Visa/Access). Do not send cash or currency. UK, BFPO and Eire customers, please allow 75p per item for postage and packing, to a maximum of £7.50. Overseas customers, please allow £1 per item.

While every effort is made to keep prices low, it is sometimes necessary to increase cover prices at short notice. 22 Books reserves the right to show new retail prices on covers which may differ from those previously advertised in the books or elsewhere.

NAME ....

ADDRESS ....

....

....

☐ I enclose my remittance for £ ______
☐ I wish to pay by Access/Visa

Card number

☐☐☐☐ ☐☐☐☐ ☐☐☐☐ ☐☐☐☐

Card expiry date

☐☐ ☐☐

Please allow 28 days for delivery. Please tick box if you do not wish to receive any additional information ☐